C

Spelling

workout

Phillip K. Trocki

Modern Curriculum Press

Cleveland · Toronto

Project Editor	Phyllis Sibbing
Editor	Linda Varju
Editorial Development, Design and Production	Publicom, Inc.
Illustrators	Yvette Banek; Randy Chewning; Roberta Collier; Ruth Linstromberg; Susan Swan; George Ulrich; Randy Verougstraete
Cover Design	John K. Crum

Acknowledgments

Grateful acknowledgment is made to the following publishers and individuals for permission to reprint copyrighted material in this book. Every reasonable effort has been made to locate the ownership of copyrighted materials and to make due acknowledgment. Any omission will gladly be rectified in future editions. ☐ The excerpts from ''Reflections'' are the first and third stanzas of the poem from I THOUGHT I HEARD THE CITY by Lilian Moore. Copyright © 1969 by Lilian Moore. All rights reserved. Reprinted by permission of Marian Reiner for the author. ☐ William Heinemann Ltd. for ''The Hairy Dog'' from PILLICOCK HILL by Herbert Asquith. ☐ ''Eight Balloons'' from A LIGHT IN THE ATTIC by Shel Silverstein. Copyright © 1981 by Evil Eye Music, Inc. ☐ ''Cars Go Fast'' from DAYS AND DAYS by Annette Wynne. Copyright, 1919, by Harper & Row, Publishers, Inc. Reprinted by permission of Harper & Row, Publishers, Inc. ☐ ''Joyful,'' FROM SUMMER TO SUMMER by Rose Styron. Copyright © 1965 by Rose Styron. All rights reserved. Reprinted by permission of Viking Penguin, a division of Penguin Books USA, Inc. ☐ ''Fall'' from THE COFFEE POT FACE by Aileen Fisher. Copyright © 1933, copyright renewed, Aileen Fisher. Reprinted by permission of the author. ☐ ''Lining Up'' by Babs Bell Hajdusiewicz. Copyright © 1986 by Babs Bell Hajdusiewicz. Reprinted by permission of the author. ☐ ''Mice'' from FIFTY-ONE NEW NURSERY RHYMES by Rose Fyleman. Copyright 1926 by the Century Company. Reprinted by permission of Doubleday, a division of Bantam, Doubleday, Dell Publishing Group, Inc. ☐ ''Roads'' from POEMS by Rachel Field. Reprinted with permission of Macmillan Publishing Company from POEMS by Rachel Field (New York: Macmillan, 1957). ☐ ''April Rain Song'' from THE DREAM KEEPER AND OTHER POEMS. Copyright 1932 by Alfred A. Knopf, Inc. and renewed 1960 by Langston Hughes. Reprinted from THE DREAM KEEPER AND OTHER POEMS by Langston Hughes, by permission of the publisher. ☐ ''Alley Cat School'' from CITY SANDWICH by Frank Asch. Copyright © 1978 by Frank Asch. Reprinted by permission of Greenwillow Books, a division of William Morrow and Co., Inc. ☐ ''The Crooked Man'' from *Children's Counting-Out Rhymes, Fingerplays, Jump-Rope and Bounce-Ball Chants and Other Rhythms*, © 1983 by Gloria T. Delamar by permission of McFarland & Company, Inc., Publishers, Jefferson, NC. ☐ ''The Circus is Coming to Town'' from *Children's Counting-Out Rhymes, Fingerplays, Jump-Rope and Bounce-Ball Chants and Other Rhythms*, © 1983 by Gloria T. Delamar by permission of McFarland & Company, Inc., Publishers, Jefferson, NC. ☐ ''I'm Really Not Lazy'' from A RUMBUDGIN. Copyright © 1970 by Arnold Spilka. ☐ ''Unscratchable Itch'' from A LIGHT IN THE ATTIC by Shel Silverstein. Copyright © 1981 by Evil Eye Music, Inc. ☐ ''Snored and Snored'' from THE LOONIEST LIMERICK BOOK IN THE WORLD by Joseph Rosenbloom © 1982 Joseph Rosenbloom. Reprinted by permission of Sterling Publishing Co., Inc., 387 Park Avenue South, New York, NY 10016. ☐ ''Me a Mess?'' by Babs Bell Hajdusiewicz. Copyright © 1986 by Babs Bell Hajdusiewicz. Reprinted by permission of the author. ☐ ''If We Didn't Have Birthdays'' from HAPPY BIRTHDAY TO YOU! by Dr. Seuss. Copyright © 1959 by Dr. Seuss. Reprinted by permission of Random House, Inc. ☐ Handwriting models in this book are reproduced with permission of Zaner-Bloser, Inc., © 1989.

Copyright © 1990 by Modern Curriculum Press

MODERN CURRICULUM PRESS, INC.
A division of Simon & Schuster
13900 Prospect Road, Cleveland, Ohio 44136

ISBN 0-8136-2809-1   6 7 8 9   96 95 94 93

Table of Contents

		Page
Learning to Spell a Word		4
Lesson 1	Consonants	5
Lesson 2	Consonants	9
Lesson 3	Hard and Soft **c** and **g**	13
Lesson 4	Short-Vowel Sounds	17
Lesson 5	Long-Vowel Sounds	21
Lesson 6	Instant Replay	25
Lesson 7	Long-Vowel Sounds	29
Lesson 8	Consonant Blends	33
Lesson 9	Consonant Blends	37
Lesson 10	**y** as a Vowel	41
Lesson 11	**y** as a Vowel	45
Lesson 12	Instant Replay	49
Lesson 13	Vowels with **r**	53
Lesson 14	Vowels with **r**	57
Lesson 15	Suffixes Added to Root Words	61
Lesson 16	Suffixes Added to Root Words	65
Lesson 17	Suffixes Added to Root Words	69
Lesson 18	Instant Replay	73
Lesson 19	Regular Plurals: Adding **s** or **es**	77
Lesson 20	Irregular Plurals	81
Lesson 21	Vowel Pairs	85
Lesson 22	Double **o**	89
Lesson 23	Silent Consonants	93
Lesson 24	Instant Replay	97
Lesson 25	/ô/	101
Lesson 26	/oi/ or /ou/	105
Lesson 27	/sh/, /th/, or /th/	109
Lesson 28	/ch/, /hw/, or /h/	113
Lesson 29	Consonant Clusters	117
Lesson 30	Instant Replay	121
Lesson 31	Consonant Digraphs	125
Lesson 32	Prefixes **un, dis**	129
Lesson 33	Prefix **re**	133
Lesson 34	Contractions	137
Lesson 35	Homonyms	141
Lesson 36	Instant Replay	145
Writing and Proofreading Guide		149
Using Your Dictionary / Pronunciation Key		150
Spelling Workout Dictionary		151

Learning to Spell a Word

1. Say the word.

2. Look at the word and say the letters.

3. Write the word with your finger.

4. Close your eyes and think of the word.

5. Cover the word and write it on paper.

6. Check your spelling.

Game Plan

The alphabet has two kinds of letters. The **vowels** are **a, e, i, o, u,** and sometimes **y** and **w.** All the other letters are **consonants.** Read the List Words. Listen for the sounds that the consonants stand for in each word.

List Words

1. fast *fast*
2. bird *bird*
3. nine *nine*
4. life *life*
5. since *since*
6. kill *kill*
7. cannot *cannot*
8. egg *egg*
9. water *water*
10. mark *mark*
11. person *person*
12. quite *quite*
13. beside *beside*
14. sister *sister*
15. forest *forest*

Warm Up

Write the List Words that have one syllable.

1. _____
2. _____
3. _____
4. _____
5. _____
6. _____
7. _____
8. _____
9. _____

Write the List Words that have two syllables.

10. _____
11. _____
12. _____
13. _____
14. _____
15. _____

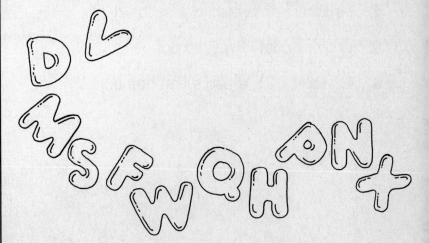

Practice

Missing Letters

Write letters to finish the List Words in the
sentences. Then write the List Words.

1. The ostrich is a large ____ i ____ ____.   _____

2. ____ i ____ e for the tallest ones is spent in North Africa.   _____

3. Some ostriches are ____ i ____ e feet tall.   _____

4. That's taller than a very tall ____ e ____ ____ o ____.   _____

5. An ostrich e ____ ____ weighs about three pounds!   _____

6. An ostrich can ____ i ____ ____ an enemy with just one   _____

   strong kick.

Word Parts

Find the compound word in each sentence. Circle
the part of the compound word that spells a List
Word. Then write the List Word on the line.

1. Breakfast is a morning meal.   _____

2. A lifeguard keeps swimmers safe.   _____

3. A bookmark keeps my place in a book.   _____

4. A robin might wash in a birdbath.   _____

5. My new coat is waterproof.   _____

6. An eggshell is a bird's first home.   _____

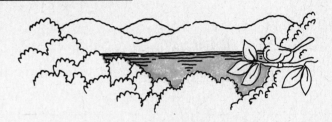

List Words

fast	kill	person
bird	cannot	quite
nine	egg	beside
life	water	sister
since	mark	forest

Alphabetical Order

Write each group of List Words in alphabetical order.

forest	quite	bird	water	egg	since	nine	mark

1. _____
2. _____
3. _____
4. _____
5. _____
6. _____
7. _____
8. _____

sister	beside	person	cannot	kill	life	fast	quite

9. _____
10. _____
11. _____
12. _____
13. _____
14. _____
15. _____
16. _____

Definitions

Write the List Word that matches the meaning given.

1. a compound word that means the opposite of <u>can</u> _____

2. a girl who is related to you _____

3. is found in ponds, rivers, and oceans _____

4. a man, woman, or child _____

5. a place filled with trees _____

Challenges

Reading and Writing

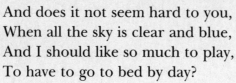

Bed in Summer

In winter I get up at night
And dress by yellow candle-light.
In summer, quite the other way,
I have to go to bed by day.

I have to go to bed and see
The birds still hopping on the tree,
Or hear the grown-up people's feet
Still going past me in the street.

And does it not seem hard to you,
When all the sky is clear and blue,
And I should like so much to play,
To have to go to bed by day?

—Robert Louis Stevenson

Describe what sights and sounds might be
outside your window on a summer night.

Bonus Words: Light

    flashlight   lantern   moonbeam   searchlight   campfire

Write a Bonus Word to label each picture.

1. _____   2. _____   3. _____

4. _____   5. _____

Consonants

Game Plan

Sometimes consonants blend together at the beginning or end of words. Listen for the blends in <u>prize</u> and <u>left</u>.
The /z/ sound can be spelled with the letter **z** as in <u>size</u> or the letter **s** as in <u>was</u>.

List Words

1.	some	*some*
2.	mostly	*mostly*
3.	four	*four*
4.	wore	*wore*
5.	was	*was*
6.	ground	*ground*
7.	left	*left*
8.	into	*into*
9.	size	*size*
10.	yell	*yell*
11.	prize	*prize*
12.	perhaps	*perhaps*
13.	rise	*rise*
14.	kept	*kept*
15.	else	*else*

Warm Up

Write each List Word under the correct heading.

/z/ sound spelled **s**

1. _____
2. _____

/z/ sound spelled **z**

3. _____
4. _____

Write the missing blends to finish List Words.

5. ____ound
6. ke____
7. le____
8. ____ize
9. perha____
10. mo____ly

Write the two List Words that rhyme with <u>pour</u>.

11. _____ 12. _____

Write the missing consonants to finish List Words.

13. i__o
14. __e__e
15. ye__
16. __o__e

9

Practice

Vocabulary

Write the List Word that matches each clue.

1. You do this when you want someone to hear you.

_____

2. You win this in a contest.

_____

3. You do this to get up from your chair.

_____

4. Two plus two equals this number.

_____

5. You walk and run on this.

_____

6. This is another word for <u>maybe</u>.

_____

Alphabetical Order

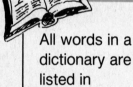

All words in a dictionary are listed in **alphabetical order.**

When you write words in alphabetical order, use these rules:

1. If the <u>first letter</u> of two words is the same, use the second letter.

2. If the <u>first two letters</u> are the same, use the third letter.

Write the List Words from the box in alphabetical order.

kept	left
yell	was
else	wore
size	mostly
into	some

1. _____

2. _____

3. _____

4. _____

5. _____

6. _____

7. _____

8. _____

9. _____

10. _____

List Words

some	ground	prize
mostly	left	perhaps
four	into	rise
wore	size	kept
was	yell	else

Scrambled Letters

Unscramble the letters to make List Words. Then use the number code to answer the riddle.

1. rnguod   __ __ __ __ __ __
                     6 7

2. sheprpa   __ __ __ __ __ __ __
                   3   2 9

3. eirs   __ __ __ __
               10 16

4. rziep   __ __ __ __ __
               12   13

5. tepk   __ __ __ __
                15   1

6. eosm   __ __ __ __
                      4

7. onit   __ __ __ __
               11 8

8. rweo   __ __ __ __
                  5   14

Find the letter with the number 1 under it. Print that letter on the line that has the number 1 under it. Do the same for numbers 2 through 16.

RIDDLE: Why isn't it fun to play hide-and-seek with a mountain?

ANSWER: Because

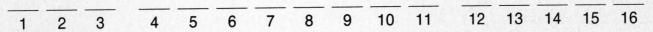

__ __ __   __ __ __ __ __ __ __ __   __ __ __ __ __ __ .
1 2 3   4 5 6 7 8 9 10 11   12 13 14 15 16

Homonyms

Write the List Word that sounds the same as the word given.

1. sum _____   **2.** for _____   **3.** sighs _____

Challenges

Reading and Writing

Look at the picture. Imagine you have bought a pair of shoes in the department store. When you get home, you discover that your new shoes give you special powers. Write a story about your shoes.

Bonus Words: Shoes
sandals   loafers   sneakers   oxfords   slippers

Write the Bonus Word that completes each sentence.

1. I wear _____ when I play tennis.

2. Dad wore brown _____ with his new brown suit.

3. Janet put a shiny penny in each of her _____.

4. My fuzzy, pink _____ keep my feet warm.

5. In the summer, my feet stay cool when I wear _____.

Hard and Soft c and g

Game Plan

Listen for the hard or soft sound in each List Word.

HARD **C**	SOFT **C**
car	city
uncle	race

The letter **g** can also stand for a hard or a soft sound.

HARD **G**	SOFT **G**
game	germ
rag	page

List Words

1. ice *ice*
2. pick *pick*
3. gone *gone*
3. case *case*
5. faces *faces*
6. cage *cage*
7. magic *magic*
8. age *age*
9. wagon *wagon*
10. give *give*
11. giant *giant*
12. once *once*
13. danger *danger*
14. places *places*
15. climb *climb*

Warm Up

Write the List Words with the hard **c** as in <u>car</u> and the hard **g** as in <u>game</u>.

HARD **C**

1. _____
2. _____
3. _____
4. _____
5. _____

HARD **G**

6. _____
7. _____
8. _____

Write the List Words with the soft **c** as in <u>city</u> and the soft **g** as in <u>page</u>.

SOFT **C**

9. _____
10. _____
11. _____
12. _____

SOFT **G**

13. _____
14. _____
15. _____
16. _____
17. _____

Practice

Vocabulary

Write the List Word that matches each clue.

1. It can carry a heavy load.   _____

2. A pet bird may live in this.   _____

3. It will make your juice cold.   _____

4. Tales may start, "___ upon a time."   _____

5. This means <u>very big</u>.   _____

6. These have eyes and mouths.   _____

7. This is the opposite of <u>take</u>.   _____

8. Do this on a ladder or a hill.   _____

9. This means <u>how old a person is</u>.   _____

10. Presto! A rabbit's in my hat!   _____

Puzzle

Write a List Word to complete each sentence.
Then read down the shaded boxes to answer the
riddle.

1. It take strong legs to ___ a mountain.

2. Tom went to many ___ on his trip.

3. The sign said, "___! Ice on Road!"

4. Jack climbed the beanstalk and met a ___.

5. The bottles of juice came in a cardboard ___.

RIDDLE: What would you need to take an
elephant for a ride on your bike?

ANSWER: ___ ___ ___ ___ ___

List Words		
ice	cage	giant
pick	magic	once
gone	age	danger
case	wagon	places
faces	give	climb

Rhyming

Write List Words that rhyme with the words given.

1. rhyme _____

2. stranger _____

3. lawn _____

4. trick _____

5. lace _____

6. tragic _____

7. twice _____

8. dragon _____

Alphabetical Order

Write each group of List Words in alphabetical order.

1. gone _____

place _____

climb _____

2. ice _____

wagon _____

faces _____

3. magic _____

give _____

cage _____

4. giant _____

age _____

once _____

Challenges

Reading and Writing

Reflections

(Excerpt)

On this street
of windowed stores
see,
in the glass
shadow people meet
and pass
and glide to
secret places.

And
now and then,
before
the window mirror
of a store,
phantom faces
stop
and window shop.

—Lilian Moore

Imagine that in passing a toy store, your eye catches the most wonderful toy. Describe what it looks like and perhaps what it does.

Bonus Words: Eye

    lens   cornea   pupil   iris   retina

Use the Bonus Words to label this diagram.

1. _____

2. _____

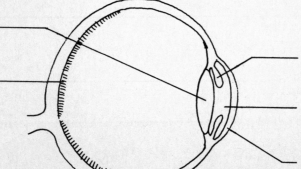

3. _____

4. _____

5. _____

Short-Vowel Sounds

Game Plan

The vowels are **a, e, i, o, u,** and sometimes **y** and **w.** Every syllable has a vowel sound. Rock has one vowel sound. Under has two. Short-vowel sounds are often spelled with just the vowel itself, but:

short **e** in head is spelled **ea,** and short **u** in does is spelled **oe.**

List Words

1. little *little*
2. its *its*
3. under *under*
4. rock *rock*
5. dead *dead*
6. past *past*
7. them *them*
8. collar *collar*
9. dug *dug*
10. does *does*
11. gobble *gobble*
12. bottom *bottom*
13. level *level*
14. felt *felt*
15. next *next*

Warm Up

Write the List Words that have one syllable.

1. _____   6. _____
2. _____   7. _____
3. _____   8. _____
4. _____   9. _____
5. _____

Write the List Words that have two syllables.

10. _____   13. _____
11. _____   14. _____
12. _____   15. _____

Practice

Dictionary

The dictionary puts an **accent mark** after the syllable with the strong sound.

per' son

Each List Word below has been divided into syllables. Say each word. Put an accent mark (') after the syllable with the strong sound. The first one has been done for you.

1. lit' tle
2. col lar
3. un der
4. bot tom
5. gob ble
6. lev el

Scrambled Letters Puzzle

Unscramble the letters to spell List words. Print one letter in each box. Then read down the shaded boxes to answer the riddle.

1. SIT

2. MOTBOT

3. STAP

4. CORK

5. TELF

6. TILLTE

7. OEDS

8. MHET

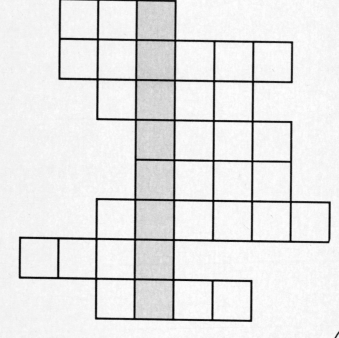

RIDDLE: What is the most famous fish of all?

ANSWER: A __ __ __ __ __ __ .

List Words

little	past	gobble
its	them	bottom
under	collar	level
rock	dug	felt
dead	does	next

Proofreading

Mario's letter has eight spelling mistakes. Circle each word that is spelled wrong. Write the words correctly on the lines.

Dear Doug,

   It's very nice on this farm. A pheasant lives in the empty lot nexct to us. It's such a pretty bird! This bird has a white coller around its neck. It also has a green head. Most of the bird's feathers are brown. They are the color of ded leaves.

   Have you ever heard a pheasant? It's voice makes a funny sound. The sound is like a gobbel. It does not sound like any other bird.

   The empty lot has a levvel field and some trees. I see the pheasant when it is in the field, but it lives under the trees. I have seen birds that dugg for worms. The pheasant does not do that. It comes out to eat the pieces of corn that we leave. It must like thim more than worms.

   I am having a good time. I will see you soon.

                              Your friend,
                              Mario

1. _____

2. _____

3. _____

4. _____

5. _____

6. _____

7. _____

8. _____

Challenges

Reading and Writing

The Woodpecker

The woodpecker pecked out a little round hole
And made him a house in the telephone pole.
One day when I watched, he poked out his head
And he had on a hood and a collar of red.

When the streams of rain pour out of the sky,
And the sparkles of lightning go flashing by,
And the big, big wheels of thunder roll,
He can snuggle back in the telephone pole.

—Elizabeth Madox Roberts

Describe another type of bird that you are familiar with. Where does it make its nest? What do you think its nest is made of?

Bonus Words: Electronics

    telephone   dial   ring   wire   cord

Complete each sentence with a Bonus Word.

1. The workers are outside fixing a fallen _____.

2. The numbers on this _____ are hard to read.

3. Why does the phone _____ when I'm in the bath?

4. Be careful you don't trip over the _____.

5. My older brother wishes he had his own _____.

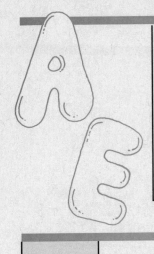
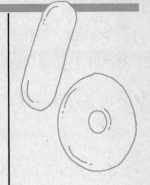

Game Plan

A **long-vowel sound** has the same sound as its letter name. The **sound-symbols** for the long vowels are:

a = /ā/   e = /ē/   i = /ī/   o = /ō/   u = /yōō/

Listen for the long-vowel sound in each List Word.

List Words

1. hello   *hello*
2. raise   *raise*
3. drive   *drive*
4. huge   *huge*
5. lines   *lines*
6. blame   *blame*
7. street   *street*
8. seat   *seat*
9. fumes   *fumes*
10. know   *know*
11. only   *only*
12. people   *people*
13. steel   *steel*
14. mail   *mail*
15. used   *used*

Warm Up

Write each List Word under the correct heading. One word will be used twice.

/ā/
1. _____
2. _____
3. _____

/ī/
4. _____
5. _____

/ō/
6. _____
7. _____
8. _____

/ē/
9. _____
10. _____
11. _____
12. _____
13. _____

/yōō/
14. _____
15. _____
16. _____

Practice

Missing Words

Write a List Word to finish each sentence.

1. The word that begins most telephone calls is _____.

2. The smell of the paint _____ is strong.

3. Look both ways before you cross the _____.

4. The bus driver will _____ you to school.

5. Most bridges today are made of _____.

6. Students _____ their hands to ask a question.

7. Hannah _____ a rubber patch to fix my tire.

8. Please put a stamp on this letter before you _____ it.

9. The _____ who drive airplanes are called pilots.

10. The elephant is a _____ animal.

Proofreading

Each sentence has two mistakes. Use the proofreading marks to fix each mistake. Then write each sentence correctly on the line.

Proofreading Marks	
⬭	spelling mistake
☰	capital letter

1. there was onle one letter in today's mail.

_____

2. Do you no where the steal mill is?

_____

3. I blaim that hooge dog for chewing my sock.

_____

4. take a seet and I will drive you to school.

_____

List Words

hello	blame	only
raise	street	people
drive	seat	steel
huge	fumes	mail
lines	know	used

Rhyming

Write List Words to rhyme with the words given.

1. tale _____

2. steeple _____

3. blooms _____

4. days _____

Puzzle

Fill in the crossword puzzle by writing a List Word to answer each clue.

ACROSS
3. a road
4. very, very big
5. to say someone did something bad
6. rows of persons or things
7. another word for <u>just</u>

DOWN
1. to lift up
2. men, women, and children
3. a chair or bench
4. a greeting

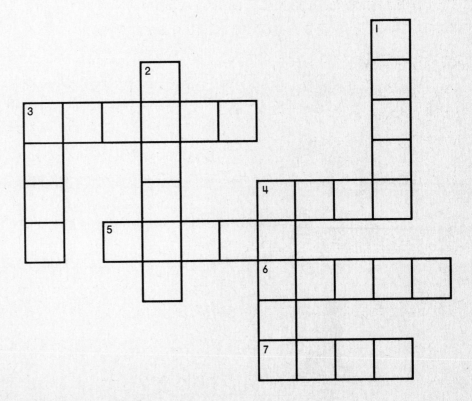

Challenges

Reading and Writing

The Hairy Dog

My dog's so furry I've not seen
His face for years and years:
His eyes are buried out of sight,
I only guess his ears.

When people ask me for his breed,
I do not know or care:
He has the beauty of them all
Hidden beneath his hair.

—Herbert Asquith

Describe your dog or a dog from a favorite story.
Draw a picture to illustrate your description.

Bonus Words: Dogs

Dalmatian   bloodhound   retriever   cocker spaniel   Great Dane

---

Complete each sentence by writing a Bonus
Word. Use clues in the picture and the sentence.

 1. The _____ is a small, friendly dog.

 **2.** A _____ is a huge, short-haired dog.

 **3.** A _____ has a very keen sense of smell.

 4. A _____ will bring back a ball that you throw.

 5. A _____ is black and white.

Game Plan

The vowels are **a, e, i, o,** and **u** (and sometimes **y** and **w**). The other letters are **consonants.** Consonants may blend together, as they do in <u>fast</u> and <u>prize</u>. Some consonants work with other letters. Listen for the sounds that **s, c,** and **g** make in <u>case, rise, ice, age,</u> and <u>give</u>.

A vowel sound may be long or short. Listen for the short vowel sounds in <u>dug, does,</u> and <u>dead</u>. Listen for the long vowel sounds in <u>hello</u> and <u>huge</u>. Notice how many ways long vowel sounds can be spelled. Listen for the long vowel sounds in <u>people, only, know,</u> and <u>dew</u>.

Practice

Each riddle has an answer with rhyming words in it. Write a List Word to finish each answer.

1. What color is paper? _____ white

2. What is an ink blot? a dark _____

3. What is next to the second hen?

a third _____

4. Where is that name? on line _____

5. What is a quick boom? a _____ blast

6. How did Mom greet a family member?

kissed her _____

Lesson I

bird   nine
sister   mark
quite   fast

_____

_____

Write each List Word under
the sound you hear in it.

both /s/ and /z/

1. _____

/z/

2. _____

3. _____

/s/

4. _____

5. _____

6. _____

Lesson **2**

some	mostly
was	size
rise	else

_____

_____

Write the List Word that
goes with each clue.

Lesson **3**

cage	wagon
give	giant
once	danger

_____

_____

1. has wheels

_____

2. pet bird's house

_____

3. threat

_____

4. hand to someone

_____

5. only one time

_____

6. huge

_____

Write the List Words in alphabetical order.

1. _____

2. _____

3. _____

4. _____

5. _____

6. _____

Lesson 4

under	dead
collar	bottom
does	level

_____

_____

Circle each List Word that is misspelled. Then write it on the line correctly.

1. You know all the poeple in this room.

   _____

2. We have a huje dog named Dinosaur.

   _____

3. Please raize your hand before you speak.

   _____

4. I can stay onlly a few days.

   _____

5. Everyone will knoe the words to this song.

   _____

6. I see a huge pile of mial on the table.

   _____

Lesson 5

raise	huge
know	mail
people	only

_____

_____

only	danger
mostly	people
giant	raise
huge	once
bird	under

Mixed Practice

Fill in each word shape with a List Word. Then follow the directions to answer the riddle.

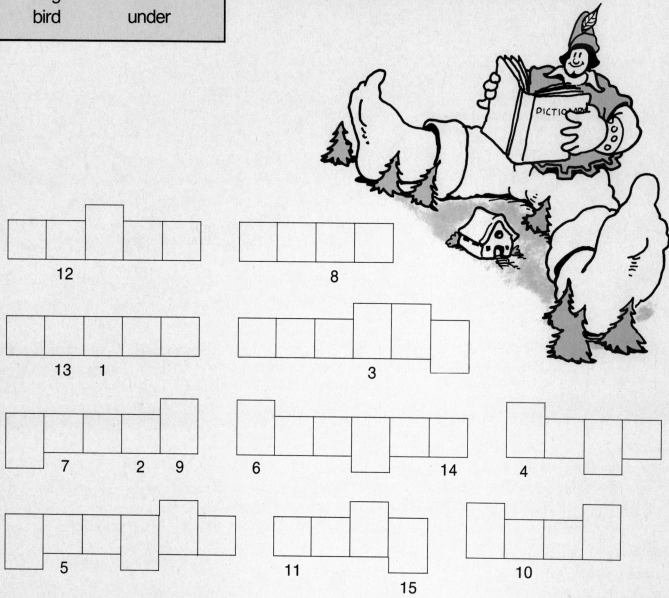

12

8

13 1

3

7   2   9

6   14

4

5

11

15

10

Find the box with the number 1 under it. Print the letter on the line with the same number. Do the same thing for numbers 2 through 15.

RIDDLE: Where can you always find money?

ANSWER: ___ ___ ___ ___ ___   ___ ___ ___ ___ ___ ___ ___ ___ ___ ___
            1   2   3   4   5   6   7   8   9   10 11 12 13 14 15

Game Plan

Words with long-vowel sounds can have different spelling patterns. The **ea** in <u>break</u> spells /ā/. The **ea** in <u>team</u> spells /ē/. The **ea** in <u>read</u> can spell /ē/ or /e/. Look at how the long-vowel sound is spelled in each List Word.

List Words

1. alive *alive*
2. human *human*
3. page *page*
4. joke *joke*
5. grind *grind*
6. inside *inside*
7. read *read*
8. seen *seen*
9. load *load*
10. music *music*
11. crazy *crazy*
12. break *break*
13. team *team*
14. east *east*
15. stone *stone*

Warm Up

Write each List Word under the correct heading.

/ā/ as in <u>day</u>

1. _____
2. _____
3. _____

/ē/ as in <u>free</u>

4. _____
5. _____
6. _____
7. _____

/ī/ as in <u>side</u>

8. _____
9. _____
10. _____

/ō/ as in <u>glow</u>

11. _____
12. _____
13. _____

/yo͞o/ as in <u>huge</u>

14. _____
15. _____

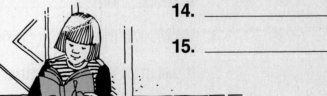

Practice

Synonyms

Write the List Word that means the same as the
word given.

1. person   **3.** viewed   **5.** burden

_____   _____   _____

2. within   **4.** rock   **6.** crack

_____   _____   _____

Missing Words

Write a List Word from the box to finish each
answer.

| alive |
| page |
| team |
| east |
| read |
| joke |

1. Why are you laughing?

She told a _____.

2. Where is the name of this book's publisher?

It is on the title _____.

3. Why do you water your plants?

It keeps them _____.

4. When will the soccer game start?

It will start when the other _____ arrives.

5. Which way did they go?

They went _____.

6. What will you do with that magazine?

I think I'll _____ it.

List Words

alive	inside	crazy
human	read	break
page	seen	team
joke	load	east
grind	music	stone

Alphabetical Order

Circle the List Words that are hiding in the puzzle. Look across and down. Write the List Words in alphabetical order.

```
S H U M A N A T
G L E U R N S E
R E A S E E N A
I N S I D E C S
N S T C R A Z M
D P A T G E A M
```

1. _____
2. _____
3. _____
4. _____
5. _____
6. _____

Proofreading

Circle the misspelled List Words in the make-believe newspaper story. Write the words correctly on the lines.

Camper Meets Dinosaur

It may sound creazy. It may seem like a jok. Last night a baby dinosaur was found alive! It was discovered by a camper insid a cave on Luck Mountain. The dinosaur had never sene a human. When the camper tried to get near, it hid behind a large stoan. The camper played cheerful muzic, and the dinosaur finally came out.

1. _____
2. _____
3. _____
4. _____
5. _____
6. _____

Challenges

Reading and Writing

Do you know how to **read music**? Music is written on the grand staff. The staff is made of lines. On the staff the notes are placed. As the notes go up on the staff, the pitch of the sound is higher. As the notes go down, the pitch of the sound is lower. Some notes look like this:

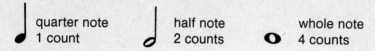

quarter note
1 count

half note
2 counts

whole note
4 counts

These notes tell you how long to sing or play the sound. Here is an example of a music piece. Music comes **alive** when you play or sing it!

Grand Staff

count: 1 2 3 4   1 2 3 4   1 2 3 4

quarter note

whole note

half note

What instrument would you like to play? What kinds of music would you play? Write two or three paragraphs to tell about the instrument you'd choose and the kind of music you'd play.

Bonus Words: Music

staff   notes   tone   scale   melody

Write a Bonus Word to match each definition.

1. set of lines and spaces on which music is written _____

2. series of notes going up or down in pitch _____

3. definite sound or pitch _____

4. symbols that show the length of a sound _____

5. main tune of a song _____

Game Plan

When two or more consonants come together in a word, they may form a **consonant blend.** In a consonant blend, you hear each letter.

Each List Word has an **s, l,** or **r** blend. The blend may be at the beginning or at the end, or at the beginning and at the end.

List Words

1. smile   *smile*
2. smart   *smart*
3. best   *best*
4. free   *free*
5. spend   *spend*
6. blind   *blind*
7. float   *float*
8. plant   *plant*
9. slumber   *slumber*
10. sting   *sting*
11. frowning   *frowning*
12. friends   *friends*
13. creek   *creek*
14. glue   *glue*
15. bring   *bring*

Warm Up

Write the List Words that begin or end with an **s** blend.

1. _____   4. _____

2. _____   5. _____

3. _____   6. _____

Write the List Words that begin with **r** blends.

7. _____   10. _____

8. _____   11. _____

9. _____

Write the List Words that begin with **l** blends.

12. _____   15. _____

13. _____   16. _____

14. _____

Practice

Antonyms

Write the List Word that means the opposite of
the word given.

1. wake _____   **4.** save _____

2. smiling _____   **5.** frown _____

3. enemies _____   **6.** worst _____

Scrambled Letters Puzzle

Unscramble the letters to spell List Words. Print
one letter in each box. Then read down the
shaded boxes to answer the riddle.

1. DLNBI

2. EGUL

3. TALNP

4. TOLAF

5. DPENS

6. ERFE

7. MILES

RIDDLE: What is at the beginning of everything,
At the end of every mile,
At the beginning of every end,
And at the end of every smile?

ANSWER: It is the _____ ____.

List Words

smile	blind	frowning
smart	float	friends
best	plant	creek
free	slumber	glue
spend	sting	bring

Definitions

Write the List Word that matches the meaning given.

1. people you like

_____

4. intelligent

_____

2. a small stream

_____

5. not able to see

_____

3. what a bee can do

_____

6. what you do to a seed

_____

Rhyming

Write a List Word to complete each rhyme.

1. Why don't you

Hand me the _____?

2. Why are you clowning

When others are _____?

3. If you need string

That's what I'll _____.

4. Later this week

I'll swim in the _____.

5. Make sure your boat

Is able to _____.

6. Why don't you see

If tickets are _____?

7. Please don't _____

On that pile of lumber.

Challenges

Reading and Writing

Eight Balloons

Eight balloons no one was buyin'
All broke loose one afternoon.
Eight balloons with strings a-flyin',
Free to do what they wanted to.
One flew up to touch the sun—POP!
One thought highways might be fun—POP!
One took a nap in a cactus pile—POP!
One stayed to play with a careless child—POP!

One tried to taste some bacon fryin'—POP!
One fell in love with a porcupine—POP!
One looked close in a crocodile's mouth—POP!
One sat around 'til his air ran out—WHOOSH!
Eight balloons no one was buyin'—
They broke loose and away they flew,
Free to float and free to fly
and free to pop where they wanted to.

—Shel Silverstein

From A LIGHT IN THE ATTIC: The Poems and Drawings of Shel
Silverstein: "Eight Balloons" copyright © 1981 by Evil Eye Music, Inc.

What else could happen to a balloon? Write a
story about other silly or serious things that could
happen to a balloon.

Bonus Words: Math

add   subtract   sum   difference   multiply

Write the Bonus Word that tells where the arrow
points.

1. $2 \times 6 = 12$ _____

4. $2 + 2 = 4$ _____

2. $2 - 1 = 1$ _____

5. $2 - 1 = 1$ _____

3. $2 + 3 = 5$ _____

Game Plan

In a **consonant blend,** you can hear the sounds of two or more letters together in a word. Listen for the blends in these words:

<u>trip</u>   <u>melting</u>   <u>spill</u>   <u>kind</u>

Find the **r, l, s,** or **n** blends in the List Words.

List Words

1. trip   *trip*
2. drove   *drove*
3. plan   *plan*
4. kind   *kind*
5. floors   *floors*
6. melting   *melting*
7. blaze   *blaze*
8. spill   *spill*
9. flowers   *flowers*
10. Friday   *Friday*
11. frozen   *frozen*
12. please   *please*
13. broken   *broken*
14. fresh   *fresh*
15. special   *special*

Warm Up

Write the List Words that have one syllable. Circle the consonant blend in each word.

1. _____   6. _____

2. _____   7. _____

3. _____   8. _____

4. _____   9. _____

5. _____

Write List Words that have two syllables. Circle the **r, s,** or **l** blend in each word.

10. _____   13. _____

11. _____   14. _____

12. _____   15. _____

Practice

Alphabetical Order

Write the List Words from the box in alphabetical order. The first and last words are done for you.

plan	kind	floors	trip	special	please
flowers	melting	drove	blaze	Friday	frozen

1. ___blaze___   5. _____   9. _____

2. _____   6. _____   10. _____

3. _____   7. _____   11. _____

4. _____   8. _____   12. ___trip___

Proofreading

Each sentence has two mistakes. Use the proofreading marks to fix each mistake. Then write each sentence correctly on the line.

Proofreading Marks
⬭ spelling mistake
≡ capital letter

1. Plese give these frech vegetables to Janie.

_____

2. The flores in rosa's house were slippery.

_____

3. frank knows that his glasses are broaken.

_____

4. Let's plan our winter tripp to Lake sunrise.

_____

5. I tried not to spil your drink, leon.

_____

List Words		
trip	melting	frozen
drove	blaze	please
plan	spill	broken
kind	flowers	fresh
floors	Friday	special

Missing Words

Write List Words to finish the story. The word
shapes will help you.

☐☐☐☐☐☐ was a ☐☐☐☐☐☐☐ day.

Dad ☐☐☐☐☐ us to the lake. The lake was

☐☐☐☐☐☐ . Inside the cabin, Mom and I lit a fire. In the morning,

the ice on the lake was ☐☐☐☐☐☐☐ . We even saw pretty

purple ☐☐☐☐☐☐☐ peeping through the snow.

Challenges

Reading and Writing

Look at the picture. Write a story that tells about where the family is going and what they will be doing on their vacation.

Bonus Words: Places to Stay
motel   inn   campsite   resort   hotel

Write the Bonus Word that matches the picture.

1. _____   2. _____   3. _____

4. _____   5. _____

y as a Vowel

LESSON
10

Game Plan

The letter **y** can team up with **a** to spell /ā/, as in <u>stay</u>. At the end of a word of more than one syllable, **y** may spell /ē/, as in <u>pretty</u>. Listen for the sound that **y** makes in each List Word.

List Words

1. lady *lady*
2. playful *playful*
3. always *always*
4. very *very*
5. empty *empty*
6. angry *angry*
7. any *any*
8. anyway *anyway*
9. maybe *maybe*
10. carry *carry*
11. family *family*
12. pretty *pretty*
13. plenty *plenty*
14. heavy *heavy*
15. hungry *hungry*

Warm Up

Write the List Words in which **y** spells the final sound /ē/.

1. _____   7. _____
2. _____   8. _____
3. _____   9. _____
4. _____   10. _____
5. _____   11. _____
6. _____

Write the List Words in which **ay** spells /ā/.

12. _____   14. _____
13. _____   15. _____

41

Practice

Dictionary

Each List Word has been divided into syllables.
Say each word. Put an accent mark (´) after the
syllable with the strong sound. Then write the List
Words.

1. ver y _____

2. la dy _____

3. car ry _____

4. an y _____

5. may be _____

6. fam i ly _____

7. an gry _____

8. heav y _____

9. an y way _____

10. emp ty _____

Word Shape Puzzle

Write a List Word in each word shape.

2

3

1   4

5   6

Use the number code to answer the riddle. Find
the letter in the box with the number 1 under it.
Print that letter on every line below that has the
number 1 under it. Do the same for numbers 2
through 6.

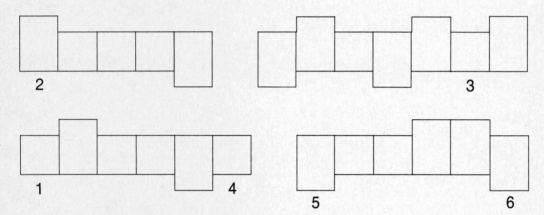

RIDDLE: What do you call a quiet little dog?

ANSWER: ___ ___ ___ ___ ___   ___ ___ ___ ___ ___
            1   2 3 4 2   5 3 5 5 6

List Words		
lady	angry	family
playful	any	pretty
always	anyway	plenty
very	maybe	heavy
empty	carry	hungry

Proofreading

Each sentence has two mistakes. Use the proofreading marks to fix each mistake. Then write each sentence correctly on the line.

Proofreading Marks	
⬭	spelling mistake
⊙	add period

1. It is allways fun to visit my uncle's ranch

_____

2. Uncle Stan likes my famly to visit

_____

3. Meybe we can take the horses for a ride

_____

4. The ladey is riding a tan horse

_____

5. This horse is verry hungery today.

_____

6. He always gets plentey of food

_____

7. His bucket for oats is emty

_____

8. My horse can carrey me all day

_____

Challenges

Reading and Writing

Cars Go Fast

Cars go fast along the street,
They're faster than the fastest feet,
And people may ride at their ease
To any little town they please.

Cars go North, South, East, and West,
(I wonder which way is the best!)
On any street they choose to be
Are people walking round like me.

Cars go along on every way
And never tire all the day;
But I should grow quite tired out
If I should always run about.
—Annette Wynne

Describe a car you would like to ride in. Tell how it looks, sounds, and feels. Tell where you would go in this car.

Bonus Words: Mechanics

    muffler   fuel   engine   brakes   bumper

Write the Bonus Word that names each part of a car or tractor.

1. _____

2. _____

3. _____

4. _____

5. _____

y as a Vowel

Game Plan

The letter **y** can spell or help spell the vowel sound /ī/ or /ē/. Look at how the /ī/ sound is spelled in <u>buy</u> and in <u>eye</u>.

At the end of one-syllable words, **y** spells /ī/, as in <u>shy</u>. At the end of a word with more syllables, **y** often spells /ē/, as in <u>army</u>.

List Words

1. army   *army*
2. anyone   *anyone*
3. twenty   *twenty*
4. shy   *shy*
5. candy   *candy*
6. dry   *dry*
7. body   *body*
8. money   *money*
9. buy   *buy*
10. honey   *honey*
11. every   *every*
12. eye   *eye*
13. sly   *sly*
14. turkey   *turkey*
15. chimney   *chimney*

Warm Up

Write the List Words in which **y** spells or helps to spell /ē/.

1. _____   6. _____
2. _____   7. _____
3. _____   8. _____
4. _____   9. _____
5. _____   10. _____

Write the List Words in which **y** spells or helps to spell /ī/.

11. _____   14. _____
12. _____   15. _____
13. _____

Practice

Rhyming

Write List Words that rhyme with the words given.

my   **funny**

1. _____   6. _____

2. _____   7. _____

3. _____   **plenty**

4. _____   8. _____

5. _____

Word Shape Puzzle

Write a List Word in each word shape.

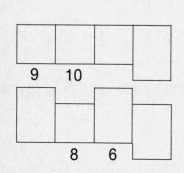

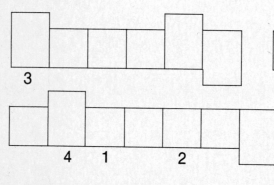

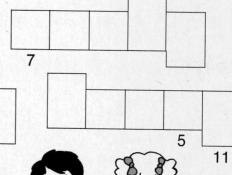

9 10

8 6   4 1 2   7   5

11

Use the number code to answer the riddle. Find the letter in the box with the number 1 under it. Print that letter on every line below that has the number 1 under it. Do the same for numbers 2 through 11.

RIDDLE: Where can you find money when your pocket is empty?

ANSWER: ___ ___ ___ ___ ___ ___ ___ ___ ___ ___ ___ ___
            1   2   3   4   5   6   1   7   3   1   8   2   9   10 11

Alphabetical Order

Write the List Words in alphabetical order under the correct letters.

a–d

1. _____
2. _____
3. _____
4. _____
5. _____
6. _____
7. _____

e–t

8. _____
9. _____
10. _____
11. _____
12. _____
13. _____
14. _____
15. _____

Definitions

Write the List Word that matches the meaning given.

1. what you use to see

_____

2. sounds just like <u>by</u>

_____

3. any person

_____

4. a big bird

_____

5. coins or bills

_____

6. sweet stuff from bees

_____

Challenges

Reading and Writing

Joyful

A summer day is full of ease,
a bank is full of money,
our lilac bush is full of bees,
and I am full of honey.

—Rose Burgunder

Describe a perfect summer morning. What would you do on this perfect morning if you could do anything at all?

Bonus Words: Science
drone   pollen   swarm   hive   beeswax

Write the Bonus Word that completes each sentence.

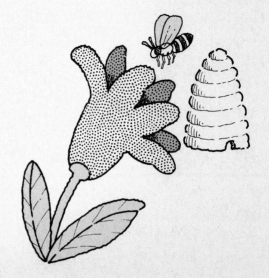

1. Bees get _____ from flowers.

2. A group of bees is a _____.

3. A _____ is a bee.

4. Many bees can live in one _____.

5. Besides honey, bees make _____.

Game Plan

The **vowels** have long and short sounds. Long vowel sounds can be spelled more than one way, as in <u>break</u> and <u>page</u>.
Consonants can be alone or come together in a word. In a **consonant blend,** you can hear the sound of each letter. Listen for the consonant blends in <u>glue</u>, <u>smile</u>, <u>best</u>, and <u>kind</u>.

In some words, **y** spells or helps spell a long vowel sound. Listen for the sound **y** spells in each of these words:

<u>playful</u>
<u>pretty</u>
<u>turkey</u>
<u>shy</u>
<u>buy</u>
<u>eye</u>

Practice

Write a List Word that means the same or almost the same as each word given.

1. crack _____

2. living _____

3. group _____

4. person _____

5. foolish _____

6. tune _____

Lesson 7

alive	crazy
human	break
music	team

_____

_____

Write a List Word that
means the opposite of
each word given.

1. sink   _____
2. worst   _____
3. take   _____
4. frown   _____
5. save   _____
6. enemies   _____

Lesson 8

smile	float
best	friends
spend	bring

_____

_____

Write a List Word that
matches each clue.

Lesson 9

kind	Friday
floors	please
blaze	special

_____

_____

1. are walked on   _____
2. not like all the rest _____
3. sweet and nice   _____
4. nice word when you ask _____
5. the last day of the school

   week   _____
6. what a fire is   _____

One word is misspelled in each set of List Words. Circle the word that is wrong. Then write it correctly on the line.

1. anyway   heavy   famly   _____

2. allways   maybe   anyway   _____

3. hungry   haevy   family   _____

4. always   maybe   aneyway   _____

5. family   hungery   always   _____

6. heavy   maybee   hungry   _____

Lesson 10

always   family
anyway   heavy
maybe   hungry

_____

_____

Write a List Word that rhymes with each word given.

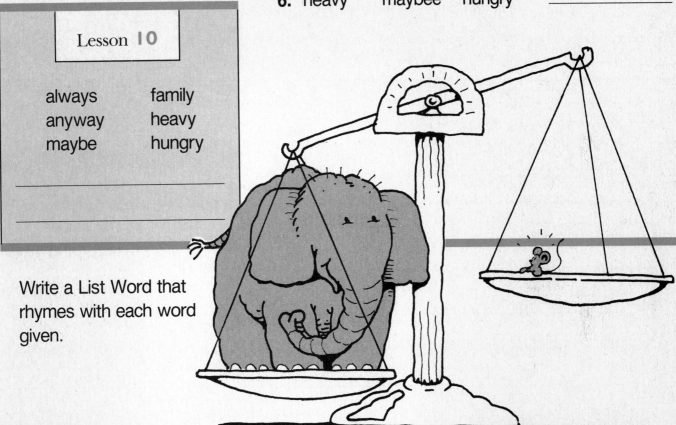

Lesson 11

anyone   money
twenty   buy
candy   turkey

_____

1. twenty-one

_____

2. plenty

_____

3. jerky

_____

4. sandy

_____

5. my

_____

6. honey

_____

human	family
anyone	please
maybe	money
special	always
buy	friends
music	heavy

Mixed Practice

Unscramble each group of words to make a sentence. The first word has a capital letter. The last word has a punctuation mark after it.

1. to   family   listen   music.   to   My   likes

_____

2. anyone   me   Can   box?   help   heavy   this   carry

_____

3. your   dinner.   Maybe   can   friends   for   stay

_____

4. day!   special   always   a   This   will   be

_____

5. shall   money?   buy   What   I   this   with

_____

6. name   human   a   eat.   might   foods   Please   that

_____

Vowels with r

Game Plan

When a vowel comes before the letter **r** in a word, the sound of the vowel can change. Each List Word contains one of the vowel sounds represented by these sound-symbols:

/är/ as in f<u>ar</u> /ôr/ as in f<u>or</u>

/ir/ as in <u>ear</u> /er/ as in <u>air</u>

List Words

1. year   *year*
2. care   *care*
3. large   *large*
4. start   *start*
5. before   *before*
6. order   *order*
7. party   *party*
8. fork   *fork*
9. cheer   *cheer*
10. chair   *chair*
11. garden   *garden*
12. morning   *morning*
13. compare   *compare*
14. clear   *clear*
15. appear   *appear*

Warm Up

Write each List Word under the correct heading.

/är/ as in f<u>ar</u>	/ir/ as in <u>ear</u>
1. _____	9. _____
2. _____	10. _____
3. _____	11. _____
4. _____	12. _____

/ôr/ as in f<u>or</u>	/er/ as in <u>air</u>
5. _____	13. _____
6. _____	14. _____
7. _____	15. _____
8. _____	

53

Practice

Sound-Spellings

Below are dictionary sound-spellings for the List Words. They show you how to pronounce the words. Use the dictionary sound-symbols in the box to read each sound-spelling. Write the List Word for each sound-spelling given.

	Dictionary Sound-Symbols
	ng = **ng** in ri<u>ng</u>
	a in <u>a</u>go /är/ as in f<u>ar</u>
	e in wat<u>e</u>r /ôr/ as in f<u>or</u>
ə =	**i** in famil<u>y</u> /ir/ as in <u>ear</u>
	o in bott<u>o</u>m /er/ as in <u>air</u>
	u in circ<u>u</u>s
	ch = **ch** in <u>ch</u>in

1. (ôr′ dər) _____

2. (bi fôr′) _____

3. (ker) _____

4. (yir) _____

5. (lärj) _____

6. (cher) _____

7. (gär′ d'n) _____

8. (fôrk) _____

9. (chir) _____

10. (pär′ tē) _____

11. (môr′ niṅg) _____

12. (stärt) _____

Proofreading

Each sentence has two mistakes. Use the proofreading marks to fix each mistake. Then write each sentence correctly on the line.

Proofreading Marks	
◯	spelling mistake
?	add question mark

1. Will we have a clair day for the party

_____

2. Let's compear a lerge dog and a small dog.

_____

3. Does the sun apear each morning

_____

54

List Words

year	order	garden
care	party	morning
large	fork	compare
start	cheer	clear
before	chair	appear

Dictionary

The top of a dictionary page has two **guide words.** The word on the left gives the first word on the page. The word on the right gives the last word on the page. The words in between are in alphabetical order.

care/cheer
care (ker) **1.** to watch over; protect **2.** to have a liking for
cart (kärt) a small wagon
cent (sent) a penny

charge (chärj)
1. to set a price
2. to attack
cheer (chir) **1.** a glad shout **2.** to make or become glad

Write the guide words on this dictionary page.

1. _____ 2. _____

Classification

Write the List Word that belongs in each group.

1. plant, flower, _____

2. knife, spoon, _____

3. day, month, _____

4. noon, night, _____

Antonyms

Write the List Word that means the opposite of the word given.

1. small _____

2. finish _____

3. cloudy _____

4. after _____

Challenges

Reading and Writing

Fall

The last of October	The last of October
We lock the garden gate.	The birds have all flown,
(The flowers have all withered	The screens are in the attic,
That used to stand straight.)	The sandpile's alone:
The last of October	Everything is put away
We put the swings away	Before it starts to snow—
And the porch looks deserted	I wonder if the ladybugs
Where we liked to play.	Have any place to go!

—Aileen Fisher

Write a letter to an imaginary pen pal. Describe your favorite fall activity.

Bonus Words: Fall

calendar	September	October	November	December

Complete each sentence by writing a Bonus Word.

1. Thanksgiving is in the month of _____.

2. The last month of the year is _____.

3. The _____ shows us the day, month, and year.

4. Columbus Day is celebrated in the month of _____.

5. The first day of autumn is in _____.

Vowels with r

Game Plan

Each List Word contains the /ur/ sound.
Look at each List Word to see which way
the /ur/ sound is spelled:

f**ir**st	pap**er**	sug**ar**
w**or**k	l**ear**n	h**ur**t

List Words

1. early *early*
2. third *third*
3. workbook *workbook*
4. first *first*
5. worry *worry*
6. hurt *hurt*
7. Saturday *Saturday*
8. better *better*
9. farmer *farmer*
10. honor *honor*
11. sugar *sugar*
12. nurse *nurse*
13. earth *earth*
14. paper *paper*
15. learn *learn*

Warm Up

Write each List Word under the correct
heading.

ir

1. _____

2. _____

ur

3. _____

4. _____

5. _____

ear

6. _____

7. _____

8. _____

er

9. _____

10. _____

11. _____

or

12. _____

13. _____

14. _____

ar

15. _____

Practice

Sound-Spellings

Below are dictionary sound-spellings for List Words. When the /ʉr/ sound is in a syllable that is not accented, the symbol /ər/ is used. Write the List Word for each sound-spelling given.

> **Dictionary Sound-Symbols**
> /ʉr/ as in <u>fur</u> and <u>her</u>
> /ə/ vowel sound in many **unaccented syllables.** It can be spelled **a, e, i, o,** or **u.**
> /oo/ as in <u>good</u> and <u>put</u>
> /sh/ as in <u>she</u> and di<u>sh</u>
> /th/ as in <u>thin</u>

1. (nʉrs) _____

2. (lʉrn) _____

3. (fär′ mər) _____

4. (hʉrt) _____

5. (fʉrst) _____

6. (än′ ər) _____

7. (shoog′ ər) _____

8. (ʉrth) _____

9. (wʉr′ ē) _____

10. (bet′ ər) _____

11. (wʉrk′ book) _____

12. (ʉr′ lē) _____

13. (thʉrd) _____

14. (sat′ ər dē) _____

Dictionary

Write the List Words that would appear on a dictionary page that has the guide words below. Make sure the words are in alphabetical order.

eye/hut

1. _____

2. _____

3. _____

4. _____

out/time

5. _____

6. _____

7. _____

8. _____

List Words

early	hurt	sugar
third	Saturday	nurse
workbook	better	earth
first	farmer	paper
worry	honor	learn

Puzzle

Fill in the crossword puzzle by writing a List Word
to answer each clue.

ACROSS

1. more excellent
8. to gain knowledge
9. There's no school today!
10. sweetener
11. high regard; fame

DOWN

2. after second
3. not late
4. book of school activities
5. person who grows crops
6. school supply
7. medical worker

Challenges

Reading and Writing

Lining Up

If I am first, then you can't be
Unless you stand in front of me.
Then I am second. I'm behind
The one who is the first in line.
If someone else now joins our line,
They will be third and stand behind.

Then fourth is next and fifth is last,
Unless we all turn around real fast.
Now who is first and who is third?
Your number changed! What is your word?

—Babs Bell Hajdusiewicz

Imagine that there are twelve children in your family. Write a story or poem about bedtime at your house.

Bonus Words: Math

| seventh | eighth | ninth | tenth | eleventh |

Write a Bonus Word to spell out each symbol.

11th   1. _____

9th   2. _____

8th   3. _____

7th   4. _____

10th   5. _____

Game Plan

A **suffix** is added at the end of a **root word**.

If a word ends in a vowel and **y**, add only the suffix.

stay + ed = stayed

If a word ends in a consonant and **y**, change the **y** to **i** before adding the suffix unless the suffix begins with **i**.

worry + ed = worried
worry + ing = worrying

List Words

1. rained   *rained*
2. prayed   *prayed*
3. studied   *studied*
4. cleaning   *cleaning*
5. thanked   *thanked*
6. acted   *acted*
7. worried   *worried*
8. helped   *helped*
9. copying   *copying*
10. flying   *flying*
11. hurried   *hurried*
12. married   *married*
13. dressing   *dressing*
14. camping   *camping*
15. replied   *replied*

Warm Up

Write the List Words. In some List Words, you must change the **y** to **i**.

1. rain + ed = _____
2. pray + ed = _____
3. study + ed = _____
4. clean + ing = _____
5. thank + ed = _____
6. act + ed = _____
7. worry + ed = _____
8. help + ed = _____
9. copy + ing = _____
10. fly + ing = _____
11. hurry + ed = _____
12. marry + ed = _____
13. dress + ing = _____
14. camp + ing = _____
15. reply + ed = _____

Practice

Classification

Write the List Word that belongs in each group.

1. teacher, tests, books

_____

5. clouds, lightning, thunder

_____

2. tent, sleeping bag, backpack

_____

6. pilot, airplane, wings

_____

3. bride, groom, ring

_____

7. soap, water, dirt

_____

4. stage, play, theater

_____

8. shirt, pants, jacket

_____

Alphabetical Order

Write the List Word that would come between
each pair of words in the dictionary.

1. ran—ruined

_____

5. under—wrecking

_____

2. hiking—ill

_____

6. hand—holding

_____

3. clue—crying

_____

7. swinging—today

_____

4. please—radio

_____

8. building—cooking

_____

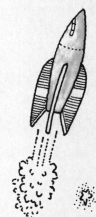

List Words

rained	acted	hurried
prayed	worried	married
studied	helped	dressing
cleaning	copying	camping
thanked	flying	replied

Missing Words

Add **ing** or **ed** to a root word in the box to make List Words. Write a List Word to finish each sentence.

help
fly
copy
rain
study
marry
act
pray

1. Because it _____, we had to cancel the picnic.

2. David _____ his dad with the housework.

3. I am _____ the words onto my paper now.

4. The farmers _____ for rain.

5. Joe _____ like a silly clown.

6. My parents got _____ right after college.

7. The pilot is _____ around the world.

8. Paul and I _____ together in the library.

Proofreading

Each sentence has two mistakes. Use the proofreading marks to fix each mistake. Then write each sentence correctly on the line.

Proofreading Marks

⬭ spelling mistake
! exclamation mark

1. Kim replyd, "I'm cleanning my room now."

_____

2. We had fun dresing for the costume party

_____

Challenges

Reading and Writing

Imagine yourself walking down the street or in a
field. Suddenly you see something strange in the
sky. Write a story to tell what happens.

Bonus Words: Science Fiction

   saucer   object   spaceship   alien   planet

Write the Bonus Word that
completes each sentence.

1. The little green man was an _____.

2. He came from the _____ Mars.

3. He arrived in a flying _____ the size of a bus.

4. I was the first to spot the strange _____ in the sky.

5. It was awesome to see the _____ land in our backyard.

Suffixes Added to Root Words

LESSON

16

Game Plan

When a short-vowel word ends with one consonant, double the consonant before adding a suffix that begins with a vowel.

swim + er = swimmer   win + ing = winning

Do not double final **x** in roots ending in **x**.

List Words

1.	swimmer	*swimmer*
2.	biggest	*biggest*
3.	winner	*winner*
4.	cutting	*cutting*
5.	foggy	*foggy*
6.	setting	*setting*
7.	stopped	*stopped*
8.	wetter	*wetter*
9.	slipped	*slipped*
10.	stepping	*stepping*
11.	beginning	*beginning*
12.	admitted	*admitted*
13.	jogger	*jogger*
14.	flexing	*flexing*
15.	waxed	*waxed*

Warm Up

Write each List Word whose final consonant was doubled before the suffix was added. Circle each suffix.

1. _____   8. _____

2. _____   9. _____

3. _____   10. _____

4. _____   11. _____

5. _____   12. _____

6. _____   13. _____

7. _____

Write each List Word that did not have the final consonant doubled before the suffix was added. Circle each suffix.

14. _____   15. _____

Practice

Suffixes

Make a List Word from the root in each sentence. Circle each root word and add a suffix from the box. Write the List Words.

ed
ing
er
est
y

1. Tom is flex his muscles. _____

2. That oak tree is the big tree in our yard. _____

3. Paula admit that she broke the vase. _____

4. My grandmother is an excellent swim. _____

5. She began set swimming records when she was ten. _____

6. The weather in Seattle is wet than in Phoenix. _____

7. The guests are begin to arrive for the party. _____

8. Dad is cut coupons out of the paper. _____

9. The mayor is step up to the microphone right now. _____

10. The car stopped to let the jog cross the street. _____

Rhyming

Write List Words that rhyme with the words given.

1. soggy _____

2. taxed _____

3. letter _____

4. clipped _____

5. logger _____

6. dimmer _____

7. dinner _____

8. chopped _____

List Words

swimmer	setting	beginning
biggest	stopped	admitted
winner	wetter	jogger
cutting	slipped	flexing
foggy	stepping	waxed

Definitions

Write the List Word that matches the meaning given. Then read down the shaded boxes to answer the riddle.

1. largest

2. misty

3. confessed

4. putting in place

5. one who moves in water

6. walking

7. polished

8. slid on something slippery

RIDDLE: What does a boat eat for breakfast?   **ANSWER:** _____

Antonyms

Write the List Word that means the opposite of the word given.

1. smallest _____   3. drier _____

2. started _____   4. ending _____

Challenges

Reading and Writing

There was a fast jogger named Chinner
Who ran races to make himself thinner.
He stopped once to eat
And slipped on a beet,
Now Chinner's no longer the winner.
                                    —Limerick

Imagine you are running in a marathon. Write
about what you see, hear, taste, smell, and feel.

Bonus Words: Cities
     Boston   Dallas   Atlanta   Denver   Los Angeles

Read the names of the states. Write the Bonus
Word that names a city in each state.

1. Georgia _____   **4.** California _____

2. Colorado _____   **5.** Massachusetts _____

3. Texas _____

Game Plan

If a word ends in silent **e**, drop the **e** before adding a suffix that begins with a vowel.

make + ing = making

Keep the final **e** when adding the suffix **ly.**

nice + ly = nicely

List Words

1. chased *chased*
2. shared *shared*
3. taking *taking*
4. living *living*
5. making *making*
6. noisy *noisy*
7. icy *icy*
8. racing *racing*
9. dancing *dancing*
10. nicely *nicely*
11. lovely *lovely*
12. closely *closely*
13. lately *lately*
14. framed *framed*
15. hoped *hoped*

Warm Up

Write List Words that tell about an action that is going on in the present. They will each have an **ing** ending. Circle the suffix at the end of each word.

1. _____ 4. _____

2. _____ 5. _____

3. _____

Write List Words that tell about an action that went on in the past. Circle the suffix at the end of each word.

6. _____ 8. _____

7. _____ 9. _____

Write List Words that end with the suffix **y.**

10. _____ 11. _____

Write List Words that end with the suffix **ly.**

12. _____ 14. _____

13. _____ 15. _____

Practice

Suffixes

Make a List Word from the root in each sentence.
Circle the root word and add a suffix from the
box. Write the List Words.

ed
ing
ly
y

1. The road was ice. _____

2. Maria has a love voice. _____

3. Mom and Dad watched the road close. _____

4. Dan nice offered to set the table. _____

5. Tom share his piece of carrot cake with me. _____

6. The loud music was make my head hurt. _____

7. Aunt Josie is live in a new city. _____

8. Kim and Jo are race to catch the school bus. _____

9. We hope that Dad would win the race, but he lost. _____

10. Pat is dance in our school play. _____

Misspelled Words

In each set of List Words one word is misspelled.
Circle the word that is wrong. Then write it
correctly on the line.

1. living   chasd   noisy   _____

2. takeing   making   racing   _____

3. frammed   lately   dancing   _____

4. shared   closely   icey   _____

5. nicely   lovly   hoped   _____

List Words

chased	noisy	lovely
shared	icy	closely
taking	racing	lately
living	dancing	framed
making	nicely	hoped

Scrambled Letters

Unscramble the letters to spell List Words. Write the List Words.

1. mardef _____

2. shcade _____

3. caingr _____

4. teally _____

5. inyso _____

6. cosylle _____

Synonyms

Write the List Word that means the same as the word given.

1. loud _____

2. beautiful _____

3. wished _____

4. followed _____

5. speeding _____

6. creating _____

Comparing Words

Read the first two underlined words in each sentence. Write the List Word that goes with the third word in the same way.

1. Quiet is to library as _____ is to circus.

2. Hot is to summer as _____ is to winter.

3. Writing is to author as _____ is to ballerina.

Challenges

Reading and Writing

Starry, quiet night
Snowflakes dancing through the dark
Fall on icy hills.

—Haiku

A haiku is a Japanese poem that tells about something in nature. It has three lines and seventeen syllables. It does not rhyme. Write a haiku about one of your favorite things in nature.

Bonus Words: Weather

snowflakes   chilly   icicles   drift   sleet

Write a Bonus Word to match each clue.

1. These are hanging pieces of frozen water. _____

2. This is a heap of snow piled up by the wind. _____

3. These are soft, white frozen crystals. _____

4. This is partly frozen rain. _____

5. This is how you feel when the weather is cold. _____

Game Plan

A vowel followed by **r** can have a special sound. Listen for the vowel sounds in <u>start</u>, <u>fork</u>, <u>cheer</u>, and <u>chair</u>. The /ur/ sound you hear in <u>hurt</u> can be spelled different ways. The vowel sound is called the **schwa** when it is found in a syllable that is not accented. Listen for the schwa in <u>farmer</u> and <u>sugar</u>.

A suffix is an addition made to the end of a word. Many times the spelling of the root word changes when a suffix is added. Look at these words:

<u>studied</u>   <u>wetter</u>
<u>taking</u>   <u>icy</u>
<u>waxed</u>   <u>closely</u>

Notice which roots were changed and which stayed the same.

Practice

Write a List Word that means the opposite of each word given.

1. after _____

2. small _____

3. vanish _____

4. finish _____

5. muddy _____

6. evening _____

Lesson 13

large	morning
start	clear
before	appear

_____

_____

Write each List Word under the number of syllables it contains.

1 Syllable

1. _____

2. _____

3. _____

2 Syllables

4. _____

5. _____

6. _____

Lesson 14	
early	sugar
first	earth
honor	learn

_____

_____

Write a List Word that matches each clue.

Lesson 15	
rained	copying
studied	hurried
worried	replied

_____

_____

1. went faster _____

2. answered the question _____

3. made the day wet _____

4. did schoolwork _____

5. doing the same thing again _____

6. bothered _____

Write this set of List Words in alphabetical order. Draw a circle around each root word.

1. _____

2. _____

3. _____

4. _____

5. _____

6. _____

Lesson 16

swimmer	slipped
biggest	beginning
winner	admitted

_____

_____

Write the List Word that means the same or almost the same as each word given.

Lesson 17

living	nicely
noisy	lovely
icy	hoped

_____

_____

1. frozen

_____

2. wished

_____

3. kindly

4. alive

_____

5. beautiful

_____

6. loud

admitted	copying
honor	start
studied	icy
sugar	large

Mixed Practice

Fill in the crossword puzzle by writing a List Word to answer each clue.

ACROSS

1. begin
2. big
4. confessed
5. respect
7. making a copy

DOWN

1. sweet food
3. read carefully
6. frozen

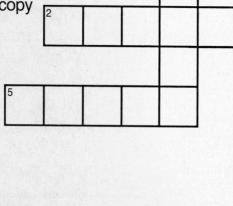

Game Plan

Singular nouns name one person, place or thing. Plurals name more than one. Add **s** to most singular nouns to make them plural.

If a noun ends in **x**, **z**, **s**, **sh**, or **ch**, add **es** to make it plural. If a noun ends with a consonant and **y**, change the **y** to **i** and add **es**.

List Words

1. cones
2. hunters
3. desks
4. babies
5. berries
6. puppies
7. bushes
8. bunches
9. brushes
10. branches
11. inches
12. taxes
13. classes
14. dishes
15. watches

Warm Up

Write each List Word under the correct heading. The heading tells what was done to a singular word to form the plural List Word.

add **s**

1. _____
2. _____
3. _____

change **y** to **i**, and add **es**

4. _____
5. _____
6. _____

add **es**

7. _____
8. _____
9. _____
10. _____
11. _____
12. _____
13. _____
14. _____
15. _____

Practice

Rhyming

Write List Words that rhyme with the words given.

1. phones _____   5. glasses _____

2. crushes _____   6. ferries _____

3. punches _____   7. pinches _____

4. notches _____   8. wishes _____

Scrambled Letters Puzzle

Unscramble the letters to spell List Words. Print one letter in each box. Then read down the shaded boxes to answer the riddle.

1. EREBRIS

2. SEATX

3. SERNBACH

4. SIABBE

5. CINSHE

6. AHETWCS

7. SKEDS

8. SIUPPEP

9. UNTRESH

RIDDLE: Why does the Statue of Liberty stand in New York Harbor?

ANSWER: ____ ____ ____ ____ ____ ____ ____.

List Words

cones	puppies	inches
hunters	bushes	taxes
desks	bunches	classes
babies	brushes	dishes
berries	branches	watches

Proofreading

Each sentence has two mistakes. Use the proofreading marks to fix each mistake. Then write each sentence correctly on the line.

Proofreading Marks

 spelling mistake

— take out word

1. The bushs have have many berries.

_____

2. The conees are in bunchs.

_____

3. I can see the hunterses check their watchs.

_____

4. Look at at those cute little puppys!

_____

5. We brought their brushs and food dishs.

_____

6. Keep the deskses twelve inchs apart.

_____

7. Babys are too young for for classes.

_____

8. The people standing there there are paying taxxes.

_____

Challenges

Reading and Writing

Imagine that you live in a cabin in the woods. Describe a delicious summer supper that you gathered yourself.

Bear in a Cave

Here is a cave, inside is a bear.
Now he comes out to get some fresh air.
He stays out all summer in sunshine and heat,
He hunts in the bushes for berries to eat.

When snow starts to fall he hurries inside
His warm little cave and there he will hide.
When spring comes again the snow melts away,
And out comes the bear, ready to play.

He stays out all summer in sunshine and heat,
He hunts in the bushes for berries to eat.

Bonus Words: Fruits

blueberries   grapes   cherries   watermelons   lemons

Use the Bonus Words to label each picture.

1. _____

2. _____

3. _____

4. _____

5. _____

Game Plan

Nouns often have **irregular plurals** that do <u>not</u> end with **s**.

deer/deer   man/men   <u>ox/oxen</u>   tooth/teeth

Singular nouns ending with **f** or **fe** often form plurals by changing **f** or **fe** to **v** and adding **es.**

List Words

1. men
2. women
3. children
4. loaves
5. teeth
6. mice
7. deer
8. sheep
9. lives
10. fish
11. leaves
12. knives
13. wolves
14. oxen
15. wives
16. heroes
17. potatoes
18. geese
19. shelves
20. cattle

Warm Up

Write the List Words that do <u>not</u> end with **s**.

1. _____   7. _____

2. _____   8. _____

3. _____   9. _____

4. _____   10. _____

5. _____   11. _____

6. _____

Write the List Words that have singular forms that end with **f** or **fe.**

12. _____   16. _____

13. _____   17. _____

14. _____   18. _____

15. _____

Write the List Words that have singular forms that end with the letter **o.**

19. _____

20. _____

81

Practice

Rhyming

Write List Words that rhyme with the words given.

1. elves _____
2. grease _____
3. zeroes _____
4. weaves _____
5. wish _____

6. deep _____
7. hear _____
8. nice _____
9. wreath _____
10. pen _____

Write the three List Words that rhyme with <u>dives</u>.

11. _____
12. _____
13. _____

Missing Words

Write a List Word to finish each sentence. Use one of the words in the box.

cattle
oxen
wolves
leaves
potatoes
loaves
children
women

1. The fall _____ are pretty colors.
2. Please buy two _____ of bread.
3. Two _____ pulled the big cart.
4. We heard _____ howling.
5. Are those _____ cows or bulls?
6. None of the _____ were parents.
7. Forty _____ ride the school bus.
8. Shall I mash or bake the _____?

List Words

men	mice	leaves	heroes
women	deer	knives	potatoes
children	sheep	wolves	geese
loaves	lives	oxen	shelves
teeth	fish	wives	cattle

Word Puzzle

Write the List Word that matches the clue given.
Then read down the shaded boxes to answer the riddle.

Here's what they can do . . .

1. swim

2. say "baa"

3. fall off trees

4. run fast

5. grow up

6. cut

7. be dads

8. lay eggs

9. be moms

10. howl at the moon

11. pull carts

RIDDLE: What should you do if you meet a hungry monster?

ANSWER: _____ _____ _____.

Challenges

Reading and Writing

Mice

I think mice
Are rather nice.
    Their tails are long,
    Their faces small,
    They haven't any
    Chins at all.
    Their ears are pink,
    Their teeth are white,
    They run about
    The house at night.
    They nibble things
    They shouldn't touch
    And no one seems
    To like them much.
But *I* think mice
Are nice.

—Rose Fyleman

Your small pet has escaped from its cage. Tell what happens and where you find your pet.

Bonus Words: House

    bedroom   basement   hallway   kitchen   pantry

Write the Bonus Word that each clue tells about.

1. under the house _____

2. where you store food _____

3. long passageway _____

4. where you cook _____

5. where you sleep _____

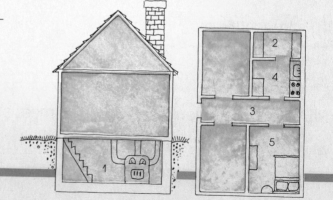

Vowel Pairs

Game Plan

In a vowel pair, the first vowel usually stands for a long sound and the second vowel is silent.
teacher = /ē/   afraid = /ā/

Some words do not follow this rule.
gr**ea**t = /ā/   gr**ou**p = /o͞o/
Vowel pairs may have a short sound.
s**ai**d = /e/   r**ea**dy = /e/

List Words

1. teacher
2. feel
3. speak
4. clue
5. fail
6. soak
7. below
8. lie
9. needle
10. said
11. group
12. feast
13. ready
14. cheap
15. again
16. throat
17. eager
18. sooner
19. least
20. contain

Warm Up

Write each List Word under the correct heading.

/ā/ as in day

1. _____
2. _____

/ē/ as in meet

3. _____
4. _____
5. _____
6. _____
7. _____
8. _____
9. _____
10. _____

/ī/ as in mile

11. _____

/ō/ as in home

12. _____
13. _____
14. _____

/e/ as in red

15. _____
16. _____
17. _____

/o͞o/ as in tool

18. _____
19. _____
20. _____

85

Practice

Antonyms

Write the List Word that means the opposite of
the word given.

1. most _____

4. later _____

2. dry _____

5. succeed _____

3. above _____

6. expensive _____

Classification

Write the List Word that belongs in each group.

1. pin, thread, _____

5. student, desk, _____

2. anxious, willing, _____

6. sit, stand, _____

3. lunch, dinner, _____

7. tongue, mouth, _____

4. ____, set, go, _____

8. crowd, mob, _____

Proofreading

Read this story. Circle any misspelled List Words.
Write them correctly on the lines.

Carlos found a clue in the park. It
sed, "On what tree will a neadle grow?
Find that tree. There you will find a box.
It will cuntane a prize!"

Carlos was eger to solve the clue. He
found his friend Rosa. "Are you reddy
for some fun?" he said. He read the
cloo aggen. She listened carefully.

"Pine needles grow on a pine tree,"
Rosa said. "Let's find a pine tree!"

They ran to the park and found a
pine tree. Bellow it they found a box.
Inside was a birthday present. Then a
grupe of friends shouted, "Happy
Birthday, Carlos!"

1. _____

4. _____

7. _____

2. _____

5. _____

8. _____

3. _____

6. _____

9. _____

List Words

teacher	soak	group	throat
feel	below	feast	eager
speak	lie	ready	sooner
clue	needle	cheap	least
fail	said	again	contain

Syllables

Write each two-syllable List Word.

1. _____
2. _____
3. _____

4. _____
5. _____
6. _____

7. _____
8. _____

Definitions

Write the List Word that matches the meaning given. Use the number code to answer the riddle. Find the letter with the number 1 under it. Put that letter on each line below with the number 1 under it. Do the same for numbers 2 through 8.

1. a person who works at a school ___ ___ ___ ___ ___ ___ ___
                                     8   1   2

2. not to win or succeed ___ ___ ___ ___
                            6

3. wanting very much ___ ___ ___ ___ ___
                       3   4

4. to say, tell, whisper, or shout ___ ___ ___ ___ ___
                                     7   5

RIDDLE: What did the goat have when it ate the dollar bill?

ANSWER: It had a ___ ___ ___ ___ ___   ___ ___ ___ ___ ___ !
                      1   2   3   4   5   6   3   4   7   8

Challenges

Reading and Writing

Roads

A road might lead to anywhere—
    To harbor towns and quays,
Or to a witch's pointed house
    Hidden by bristly trees.
It might lead past the tailor's door,
    Where he sews with needle and thread,
Or by Miss Pim the milliner's,
    With her hats for every head.

It might be a road to a great, dark cave
    With treasure and gold piled high,
Or a road with a mountain tied to its end,
    Blue-humped against the sky.
Oh, a road might lead you anywhere—
    To Mexico or Maine.
But then, it might just fool you, and—
    Lead you back home again!

—Rachel Field

What kind of shop might you own in this village?
Write a story to tell about your shop.

Bonus Words: States				
Maine	Michigan	New York	Texas	Alaska

Write a Bonus Word to match each map.

1. _____   **2.** _____   **3.** _____

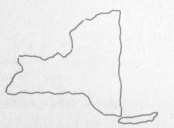

4. _____   **5.** _____

The cool goose has a good book.

Game Plan

The vowel pair **oo** stands for three sounds.
/o͞o/ as in cool   /o͝o/ as in book
/u/ as in flood
Listen for which sound the vowel pair **oo** stands for in each List Word.

Warm Up

Write each List Word under the correct heading.

List Words		

1. scoop
2. shoot
3. afternoon
4. cooler
5. roof
6. broom
7. pool
8. choose
9. goose
10. soothe
11. loose
12. stood
13. goodness
14. wool
15. brook
16. cookie
17. goodbye
18. wooden
19. soot
20. blood

/o͞o/ as in cool

1. _____
2. _____
3. _____
4. _____
5. _____
6. _____
7. _____
8. _____
9. _____
10. _____
11. _____

/o͝o/ as in book

12. _____
13. _____
14. _____
15. _____
16. _____
17. _____
18. _____
19. _____

/u/ as in flood

20. _____

Practice

Definitions

Write the List Word that matches the meaning given.

1. to pick _____

2. a bird _____

3. a dessert _____

4. place to swim _____

5. a small stream _____

6. fluid in the body _____

7. a black powder _____

8. part of a day _____

Alphabetical Order

Write each group of six List Words in alphabetical order.

loose	goose	goodbye
cooler	cookie	choose

soothe	wooden	scoop
shoot	stood	wool

1. _____

2. _____

3. _____

4. _____

5. _____

6. _____

7. _____

8. _____

9. _____

10. _____

11. _____

12. _____

Rhyming

Write List Words to rhyme with the words given.

1. put _____

2. cool _____

3. mud _____

4. group _____

5. room _____

6. look _____

7. boot _____

8. good _____

9. shoes _____

List Words

scoop	broom	loose	cookie
shoot	pool	stood	goodbye
afternoon	choose	goodness	wooden
cooler	goose	wool	soot
roof	soothe	brook	blood

Proofreading

The Old Mill Restaurant needs your help! Circle the misspelled List Words in this advertisement. Write the words correctly on the lines.

     At the **Old Mill,** we serve lunch each aftanune between noon and four o'clock on our outside deck. Choes our famous fresh fish or roast guse! For dessert, order a skupe of homemade ice cream and a fresh-baked coockey!

     Here at the **Old Mill,** we are known for the gudness of our foods. But that's not all! Our quiet woodland setting will soth you. Sitting by our broke, you'll think the city is miles away. People who dine at the **Old Mill** come back time after time. They hate to say gudby!

1. _____ 4. _____ 7. _____

2. _____ 5. _____ 8. _____

3. _____ 6. _____ 9. _____

Comparing Words

Read the first two underlined words in each sentence. Write the List Word that goes with the third word in the same way.

1. Come is to leave as hello is to _____.

2. Hot is to cold as warmer is to _____.

3. Snow is to shovel as dirt is to _____.

4. Head is to hat as building is to _____.

Challenges

Reading and Writing

April Rain Song

Let the rain kiss you.
Let the rain beat upon your head with
   silver liquid drops.
Let the rain sing you a lullaby.

The rain makes still pools on the sidewalk.
The rain makes running pools in the gutter.
The rain plays a little sleep-song on our
   roof at night—
And I love the rain.

—Langston Hughes

Imagine that it's raining. You and a friend have to play inside. Tell how you spend the long afternoon.

Bonus Words: Rain

raincoat   waterproof   storm   showers   puddle

Write a Bonus Word to complete each sentence.

1. A bad _____ swept through the city last night.

2. Boots that are _____ will keep your feet dry.

3. Wear a _____ to keep your body dry.

4. If you splash your feet in a _____ , you might get soaked!

5. Gentle spring _____ help the flowers grow.

Silent Consonants

Game Plan

In each List Word you will find that **gh** or **l** is not heard.
Look for these spelling patterns in your List Words:

al is /a/ as in <u>hat</u>   **eigh** is /ā/ as in <u>ate</u>

igh is /ī/ as in <u>kite</u>   **ough** is /o͞o/ as in <u>soon</u>

oul is /o͝o/ as <u>wood</u>   **ough** is /ô/ as in <u>saw</u>

List Words

1. fight
2. half
3. sight
4. would
5. night
6. light
7. calf
8. might
9. highway
10. moonlight
11. bright
12. eight
13. thought
14. through
15. weight
16. fright
17. sigh
18. slight
19. fought
20. knight

Warm Up

Write each List Word under the correct heading.
Circle the silent consonants in each word.

igh spells /ī/

1. _____
2. _____
3. _____
4. _____
5. _____
6. _____
7. _____
8. _____
9. _____
10. _____
11. _____
12. _____

al spells /a/

13. _____
14. _____

oul spells /o͝o/

15. _____

eigh spells /ā/

16. _____
17. _____

ough spells /o͞o/

18. _____

ough spells /ô/

19. _____
20. _____

93

Practice

Words in Words

One word in each sentence contains a form of a
List Word. Circle the List Word and then write it.
The first one has been done for you.

1. What a (frightful) accident we saw this afternoon! _____**fright**_____

2. This bag of apples weighs slightly over three pounds. _____

3. How thoughtful it was of Todd to bring a gift! _____

4. The firefighters battled the blaze all day. _____

5. My dog is afraid of lightning. _____

6. They wandered throughout the forest for three days. _____

7. "On behalf of the voters, I thank you," the mayor said. _____

8. "That's a mighty pretty horse," the cowboy said. _____

Dictionary

Write the List Word for each sound-spelling given.

1. (fôt) _____

2. (wāt) _____

3. (brīt) _____

4. (wood) _____

5. (kaf) _____

6. (throo) _____

7. (haf) _____

8. (hī′ wā) _____

9. (sīt) _____

10. (āt) _____

11. (thôt) _____

12. (frīt) _____

13. (moon′ līt) _____

14. (sī) _____

List Words

fight	light	bright	fright
half	calf	eight	sigh
sight	might	thought	slight
would	highway	through	fought
night	moonlight	weight	knight

Homonyms

Write two List Words that are homonyms.

1. _____ 2. _____

Words that sound alike but are spelled differently are called **homonyms.**

Write the List Word that sounds the same as the word given.

3. ate _____   4. wait _____

Puzzle

Fill in the crossword puzzle.

ACROSS

2. an idea
4. 4 + 4
6. opposite of day
7. main road
9. view
10. You see this when the sun is down.

DOWN

1. in one side and out the other
3. how heavy something is
5. a lamp
8. homonym for wood

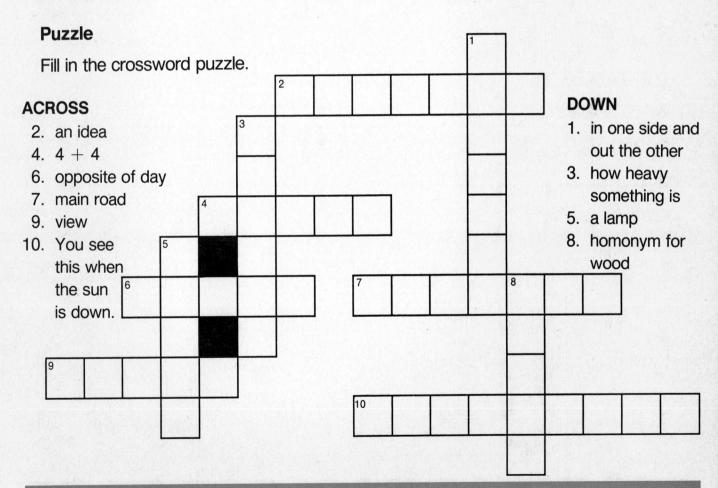

Challenges

Reading and Writing

Alley Cat School

Do alley cats go
    to alley cat school?
Where they learn how to slink
    and stay out of sight?
Where they learn how to find
    warm and comfortable places,
On a cold wintry night?

Do they learn from teachers and books,
    how to topple a garbage can lid?
Did they all go
    to alley cat school?
Is that what they did?

—Frank Asch

Write a story about an animal school. What animals go there? What kinds of things do they learn there? Be as funny or as serious as you like.

Bonus Words: School

    health   gym   spelling   arithmetic   science

Write the Bonus Word that matches the picture clue.

1. _____

2. _____

3. _____

4. _____

5. _____

Game Plan

Just add **s** to most nouns to make them plural. If the noun ends in **x, z, s, sh,** or **ch,** add **es,** as in <u>taxes</u> and <u>branches</u>. If a noun ends in a consonant and **y,** change the **y** to **i** before you add the **es,** as in <u>babies</u>. Some plural nouns, such as <u>men</u>, <u>deer</u>, <u>leaves</u>, and <u>heroes</u>, are irregular. They may change their spellings or endings.

Most vowel pairs spell long vowel sounds, as in <u>feast</u>. A few words, like <u>said</u>, do not follow this rule. Some vowel pairs spell short vowel sounds, as in <u>again</u>. The vowels **oo** can stand for three sounds. Listen for the sounds in <u>scoop</u>, <u>stood</u>, and <u>blood</u>. In words such as <u>calf</u>, silent consonants are part of the vowel sound.

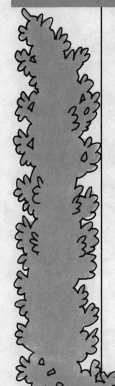

Practice

Write the List Words in alphabetical order.

Lesson 19	
inches	bushes
desks	puppies
watches	babies

1. _____   4. _____

2. _____   5. _____

3. _____   6. _____

Write each List Word under
the correct heading.

animals

1. _____

2. _____

3. _____

people

4. _____

5. _____

6. _____

Lesson 20

children	wolves
geese	heroes
sheep	women

_____

_____

Write a List Word that
rhymes with each word
given.

Lesson 21

group	speak
soak	said
clue	least

_____

_____

1. fed

_____

2. peek

_____

3. feast

_____

4. poke

_____

5. loop

_____

6. flew

_____

Write each List Word under the word with the same vowel sound.

scoop   **good**

1. _____   4. _____

2. _____   5. _____

3. _____   6. _____

Lesson 22

shoot   stood
brook   cookie
choose   soothe

_____

_____

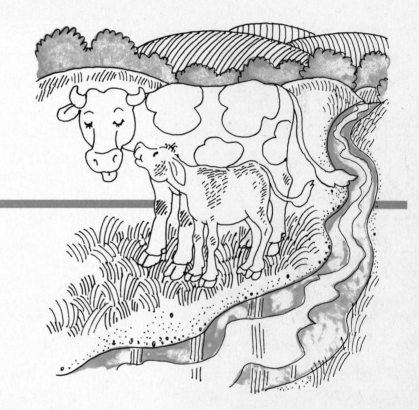

Write a List Word that matches each clue.

Lesson 23

fight   would
calf   highway
eight   fright

_____

_____

1. a number

_____

2. argue

_____

3. kind of road

_____

4. sounds like <u>wood</u>

_____

5. feeling of fear

_____

6. baby cow

_____

heroes	eight
fright	speak
group	puppies
least	choose
children	

Mixed Practice

Fill in each shape with a List Word. Then follow the directions to answer the riddle.

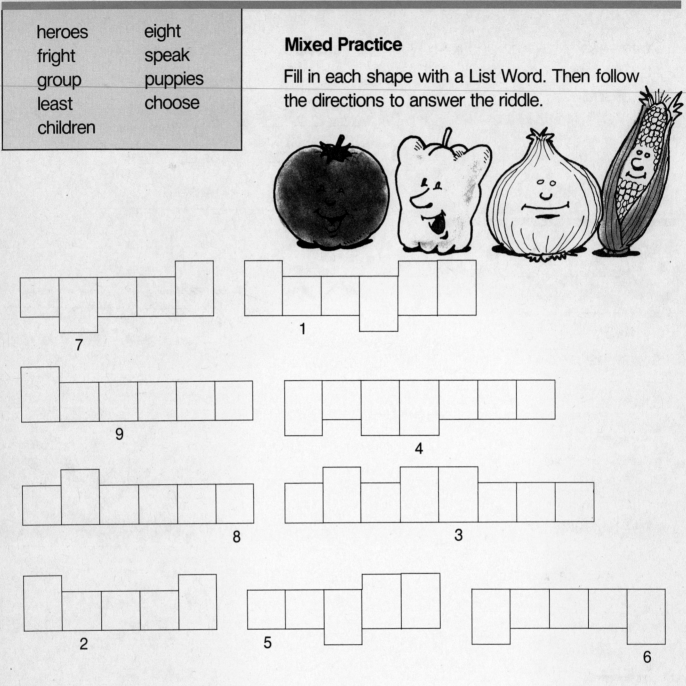

Find the box with number 1 under it. Print that letter on the line below that has number 1 under it. Then do the same for numbers 2 through 9.

RIDDLE: What stays hot, even in the freezer?

ANSWER: ___ ___ ___ ___ ___ ___ ___ ___ ___
            1   2   3   4   5   6   7   8   9

Game Plan

The /ô/ sound can be spelled many ways:

au as in <u>because</u>   **aw** as in <u>flaw</u>

o as in <u>cost</u>   **ou** as in <u>bought</u>

a followed by **l** as in <u>already</u>

Look at the spelling of /ô/ in each List Word.

List Words

1. already
2. because
3. almost
4. flaw
5. cost
6. wallet
7. laws
8. lost
9. long
10. belong
11. across
12. all right
13. bought
14. August
15. chalk
16. haul
17. awful
18. crawl
19. lawn
20. caught

Warm Up

Write each List Word under the correct spelling of its /ô/ sound.

au

1. _____   3. _____

2. _____   4. _____

aw

5. _____   8. _____

6. _____   9. _____

7. _____

a followed by **l**

10. _____   13. _____

11. _____   14. _____

12. _____

o or **ou**

15. _____   18. _____

16. _____   19. _____

17. _____   20. _____

Practice

Dictionary

Write the List Word for each sound-spelling given.

1. (chôk) _____
2. (flô) _____
3. (lôz) _____
4. (bôt) _____
5. (lông) _____
6. (lôst) _____
7. (kôst) _____
8. (ôl red′ ē) _____
9. (ố fəl) _____
10. (krôl) _____

11. (bi lông′) _____
12. (kôt) _____
13. (wôl′ it) _____
14. (ôl′mōst) _____
15. (ô′ gəst) _____
16. (ôl rīt′) _____
17. (bi kôz′) _____
18. (hôl) _____
19. (lôn) _____
20. (ə krôs′) _____

Rhyming

Write a List Word to complete each rhyme.

1. The fish fought it,

   but I _____ it.

2. Your beautiful song

   is terribly _____.

3. I lost the pot.

   It _____ a lot!

4. Please don't talk.

   Write with _____.

5. This nice saw

   has no _____.

List Words

already	wallet	across	haul
because	laws	all right	awful
almost	lost	bought	crawl
flaw	long	August	lawn
cost	belong	chalk	caught

Word Shape Puzzle

Write a List Word in each word shape. Use the
number code to answer the riddle.

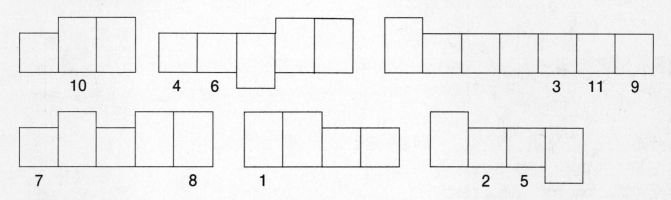

10   4   6   3   11   9

7   8   1   2   5

RIDDLE: What has four heads and four tails?

ANSWER: __ __ __ __   __ __ __ __ __ __ __
             1   2   3   4   5   6   7   8   9   10   11

Definitions

Write the List Word that
matches the meaning given.

1. rules people must obey

_____

2. missing

_____

3. okay

_____

4. not quite

_____

5. where you keep your money

_____

6. what you write with on the board

_____

Challenges

Reading and Writing

The Crooked Man

There was a crooked man,
And he walked a crooked mile.
He found a crooked sixpence,
Against a crooked stile.
He bought a crooked cat,
Which caught a crooked mouse,
And they all lived together
In a little crooked house.

—Mother Goose Rhyme

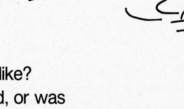

What do you think the man's house was like?
Were all the houses on the street crooked, or was
his the only one? Were parts of the house
straight? Describe the house and its yard.

Bonus Words: Money

    bank   savings   loan   teller   cash

Write the Bonus Word that completes each
sentence.

1. I don't have _____, but I can write a check.

2. The _____ is open Monday through Saturday.

3. We needed a _____ so we could buy our house.

4. I put five dollars into my _____ account yesterday.

5. Ask the _____ to give the money in change.

Game Plan

The /oi/ sound may be spelled **oy** as in <u>toy</u> or **oi** as in <u>coin</u>. The /ou/ sound may be spelled **ow** as in <u>town</u> or **ou** as in <u>proud</u>.

Each List Word has the /oi/ or /ou/ sound. Look at how the sound is spelled in each List Word.

List Words

1. clown
2. join
3. town
4. crowd
5. enjoy
6. round
7. loud
8. point
9. coin
10. toys
11. about
12. proud
13. allow
14. foil
15. power
16. pound
17. blouse
18. crown
19. choice
20. loyal

Warm Up

Write each List Word under the correct heading.

oi as in <u>oil</u>

1. _____
2. _____
3. _____
4. _____
5. _____

ow as in <u>how</u>

6. _____
7. _____
8. _____
9. _____
10. _____
11. _____

oy as in <u>boy</u>

12. _____
13. _____
14. _____

ou as in <u>sound</u>

15. _____
16. _____
17. _____
18. _____
19. _____
20. _____

The **proud clown** has a **toy coin**.

105

Practice

Word Building

Build List Words by adding or subtracting letters.
Write the List Words.

1. enter − ter + joy = _____

2. alone − one + low = _____

3. black − ack + ouse = _____

4. crown − n + d = _____

5. pouch − ch + nd = _____

6. above − ove + out = _____

7. boys − b + t = _____

8. voice − v + ch = _____

9. cloud − c = _____

10. joint − j + p = _____

11. royal − r + l = _____

12. brown − br + t = _____

Proofreading

Each sentence has two mistakes. Use the proofreading marks to fix each mistake. Then write each sentence correctly on the line.

Proofreading Marks	
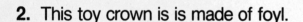	spelling mistake
—	take out word

1. The cloun will joyn the show.

   _____

2. This toy crown is is made of foyl.

   _____

3. The king is prowd of of his power.

   _____

4. Each coyn is rownd.

   _____

5. Every team needs a a croud of loyal fans.

   _____

List Words

clown	round	about	pound
join	loud	proud	blouse
town	point	allow	crown
crowd	coin	foil	choice
enjoy	toys	power	loyal

Alphabetical Order

Write each group of List Words in alphabetical order.

join	allow	about
enjoy	round	coin

toys	town	power
pound	point	proud

1. _____ 4. _____   1. _____ 4. _____

2. _____ 5. _____   2. _____ 5. _____

3. _____ 6. _____   3. _____ 6. _____

Rhyming

A doll that is a boy might be a <u>toy boy</u>. Write a List Word that rhymes with the clue word to complete these silly definitions.

1. A place where funny people live is a <u>clown</u> _____.

2. A group of noisy people is a _____ <u>crowd</u>.

3. A monster who cooks and eats metal things might <u>boil</u> _____.

4. A cloud that is pleased with itself is a _____ <u>cloud</u>.

5. A sad or angry king might wear a <u>frown</u> _____.

6. A king who is true to his country is a _____ <u>royal</u>.

7. A king who rules from the top of a castle has <u>tower</u> _____.

Challenges

Reading and Writing

The Circus Is Coming to Town

The circus is coming to town—
There'll be a long parade;
The circus is coming to town—
There'll be pink lemonade.
The circus is coming to town—
There'll be a big brass band;
The circus is coming to town—
There'll be a popcorn stand.
The circus is coming to town—
There'll surely be a clown;

The circus is coming to town—
With a clown and merry-go-round.
The circus is coming to town—
There's a dog and pony show;
The circus is coming to town—
Let's go. . .
Let's go. . .
Let's go.

—Louise Abney

You've just been hired by a circus! Describe your
job and tell why you enjoy it.

Bonus Words: Circus

circus   parade   juggle   trapeze   acrobat

Write a Bonus Word to complete each sentence.
Use each word only once.

1. The circus _____ marched through town.

2. I love to see the dancing bears at the _____.

3. At the circus, we saw a man _____ four flaming hoops.

4. The _____ leaped into the air.

5. A swing that is high up in the air is called a _____.

Game Plan

The consonant pairs **sh** and **th** are called **consonant digraphs.** They spell the special sounds you hear in short, rush, thumb, and that. Listen for the sounds the letters **sh** and **th** spell in the List Words.

List Words

1. *short*
2. *thaw*
3. *sharp*
4. *thirty*
5. *fourth*
6. *fifth*
7. *rush*
8. *dash*
9. *than*
10. *that*
11. *thinking*
12. *push*
13. *shape*
14. *thirteen*
15. *finish*
16. *thumb*
17. *sixth*
18. *shadow*
19. *shine*
20. *shovel*

Warm Up

Write the List Words that begin with **sh**.

1. _____   4. _____

2. _____   5. _____

3. _____   6. _____

Write the List Words that end with **sh**.

7. _____   9. _____

8. _____   10. _____

Write the List Words that begin with **th**.

11. _____   15. _____

12. _____   16. _____

13. _____   17. _____

14. _____

Write the List Words that end with **th**.

18. _____   20. _____

19. _____

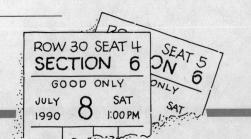

ROW 30 SEAT 4
SECTION 6
GOOD ONLY
JULY 8 SAT
1990 1:00 PM

Practice

Rhyming

Read each clue. Write List Words that rhyme with the words given.

1. Do this to catch a bus.
It rhymes with <u>mash</u>.

_____

2. Use this word to compare things.
It rhymes with <u>man</u>.

_____

3. This helps you grab things.
It rhymes with <u>numb</u>.

_____

4. Do this when you're late.
It rhymes with <u>hush</u>.

_____

5. Do this when the door is stuck.
It rhymes with <u>bush</u>.

_____

6. Use this word to point out something.
It rhymes with <u>bat</u>.

_____

7. Do this to clay.
It rhymes with <u>tape</u>.

_____

8. Do this when you are using your mind.
It rhymes with <u>winking</u>.

_____

Dictionary

Write the List Words that would appear on a dictionary page that has the **guide words** shown. Make sure the words are in alphabetical order.

1. _____

2. _____

3. _____

4. _____

5. _____

6. _____

7. _____

8. _____

shape/thinking

shape (shāp) *n.* the way a thing looks because of its outline; outer form; figure [The cloud had the *shape* of a lamb.] ◆ *v.* to give a certain shape to; form [The potter *shaped* the clay into a bowl.] —**shaped, shap´ing**

share (sher) *n.* a part that each one of a group gets or has [your *share* of the cake; my *share* of the blame]. ◆ *v.* to have a share of with others; have or use together [The three of you will *share* the back seat.] —**shared, shar´ing**—

sharp (shärp) *adj.* **1** having a thin edge for cutting, or a fine point for piercing [a *sharp* knife; a *sharp* needle]. **2** very clever or shrewd [a *sharp* mind]. ◆ *adv.* exactly or promptly [She gets up at 6:30 *sharp*.] —**sharp´ly** *adv.* —**sharp´ness** *n.*

sheep (shēp) *n.* an animal that chews its cud and is related to the goat. Its body is covered with heavy wool and its flesh is used as food, called mutton. *pl.* sheep

shine (shīn) *v.* **1** to give off light or reflect light; be bright [The sun *shines*. Her hair *shone*.]

shoot (shoot) *v.* to send a bullet, arrow, etc. from [to *shoot* a gun.] —**shot, shoot´ing** ◆ *n.* a new growth; sprout. —**shoot´er** *n.*

short (shôrt) *adj.* **1** not measuring much from end to end or from beginning to end; not long [a *short* stick; a *short* trip; a *short* novel; a *short* wait]. **2** not tall; low [a *short* tree] **3** less or having less than what is enough or correct [Our supply of food is *short*. We are *short* ten dollars.] **4** taking a shorter time to say than other sounds [The "e" in "bed" and the "i" in "rib" are *short*.] *adv.* so as to be short [Cut your speech *short*. We fell *short* of our goal.] ◆ *v.* to give less than what is needed, usual, etc. [The cashier *shorted* the customer a dollar.]

should·n't (shood´'nt) should not

shov·el (shuv´'l) *n.* a tool with a broad scoop and a handle, for lifting and moving loose material. ◆ *v.* to lift and move with a shovel [to *shovel* coal.] —**shov´eled** or **shov´elled, shov´el·ing** or **shov´el·ling**

List Words

short	fifth	thinking	thumb
thaw	rush	push	sixth
sharp	dash	shape	shadow
thirty	than	thirteen	shine
fourth	that	finish	shovel

Synonyms

Write the List Word that means the same as the word or numeral given.

1. scoop _____

2. 5th _____

3. glow _____

4. 4th _____

5. end _____

6. melt _____

7. pointed _____

8. 30 _____

9. 13 _____

10. darkness _____

Proofreading

Circle the misspelled List Words in Nina's diary entry. Write the words correctly on the lines.

Dear Diary,
Today Arlene, Carrie, and I were in a race. It was harder then I thought. I had to really puch myself to keep going. My older sister, who is thurteen, was cheering for me. That made me stay in the race. Then suddenly, I got a sharp pain in my side. I was tinking a lot about quitting. Then, I saw the finishe line. I made one last dash and crossed it. Wow! I was so tired my shadoe felt heavy. Guess what? Arlene and Carrie came in fith and sixth. I came in foreth! Bye for now.

Nina

1. _____

2. _____

3. _____

4. _____

5. _____

6. _____

7. _____

8. _____

Challenges

Reading and Writing

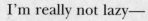

I'm Really Not Lazy

I'm really not lazy—
I'm not!
I'm not!
It's just that I'm thinking
And thinking
And thinking
A lot!

It's true I don't work
But I can't!
I just can't!
When I'm thinking
And thinking
And thinking
A lot!

—Arnold Spilka

What kind of work would you like to do? Would
you like to be the captain of a ship? Would you
like to dig for ancient treasure? Tell what you
would like to do someday and why.

Bonus Words: Grammar

verb   noun   sentence   period   comma

Write Bonus Words to complete the diagram.

1. _____ 2. _____ 3. _____ 4. _____

Paul, look at your shadow on the sand.

5. _____

/ch/, /hw/, or /h/

Game Plan

Consonant digraphs are pairs of consonants, such as **ch** or **wh**, that make one sound when they are written together in a syllable.

You can hear the sound of /ch/ in <u>each</u> and the sound of /hw/ in <u>what</u>. In <u>who</u> and <u>whole</u>, the **w** is silent, but you hear the **h**.

Warm Up

Write each List Word under the correct sound of its consonant digraph. One word will be used twice.

List Words

1. wheel
2. whale
3. everywhere
4. which
5. each
6. check
7. while
8. chewy
9. rich
10. chapter
11. chart
12. catch
13. whisper
14. who
15. whole
16. bench
17. whisk
18. whack
19. whether
20. pinch

/ch/

1. _____ 6. _____
2. _____ 7. _____
3. _____ 8. _____
4. _____ 9. _____
5. _____ 10. _____

/hw/

11. _____ 16. _____
12. _____ 17. _____
13. _____ 18. _____
14. _____ 19. _____
15. _____

/h/

20. _____ 21. _____

Practice

Dictionary

Write the List Word for each sound-spelling given.

Review some sound-symbols.
/ə/ is a soft sound spelled with any vowel in a syllable that is not accented.
/ā/ /ē/ /ī/ /ō/ /ū/ are long vowels.

/ch/ as in <u>such</u>
/hw/ as in <u>what</u>
/o͞o/ as in <u>moon</u>
/er/ as in <u>air</u>

1. (rich) _____

2. (cho͞o′ ē) _____

3. (hwis′ pər) _____

4. (ev′ rē hwer) _____

5. (hwich) _____

6. (hweth′ ər) _____

7. (ho͞o) _____

8. (hōl) _____

9. (hwisk) _____

10. (hwīl) _____

11. (hwak) _____

12. (pinch) _____

Classification

Write the List Word that belongs with the words given.

1. chair, couch, _____

2. book, page, _____

3. pitch, hit, _____

4. dolphin, porpoise, _____

Rhyming

Write List Words that rhyme with the words given.

1. peach _____

2. deck _____

3. meal _____

4. start _____

List Words

wheel	check	chart	bench
whale	while	catch	whisk
everywhere	chewy	whisper	whack
which	rich	who	whether
each	chapter	whole	pinch

Scrambled Letters

Unscramble the letters to make List Words. Then use the number code to answer the riddle.

1. h i r c   __ __ __ __
                       10

2. o h w   __ __ __
                 4

3. l o w e h   __ __ __ __ __
                   9   3

4. t h e w r e h   __ __ __ __ __ __ __
                                   2

5. p r i w s e h   __ __ __ __ __ __ __
                            6

6. e l e h w   __ __ __ __ __
              1   7

7. c h i n p   __ __ __ __ __
                  5

8. h a w e l   __ __ __ __ __
               8   11

Find the letter with the number 1 under it. Print that letter on the line below that has the number 1 under it. Do the same for numbers 2 through 11.

RIDDLE: What do you say when you meet three monsters?

ANSWER: __ __ __ __ __   __ __ __ __ __ __   __ __ __
                1   2   3   3   4   5   6   7   8   9   10   11   7   8   9

Challenges

Reading and Writing

The Codfish

The codfish lays ten thousand eggs,
    The homely hen lays one.
The codfish never cackles
    To tell you what she's done.
And so we scorn the codfish,
    While the humble hen we prize,
Which only goes to show you
    That it pays to advertise.

What would you like to advertise? Write an advertisement for a real or a made-up book, movie, television show, or song. Give the name of your product and tell why people will like it.

Bonus Words: Advertising

    advertise   slogan   billboard   coupon   sample

Write the Bonus Word that completes each sentence.

I drink milk to keep fit.

1. This _____ takes fifty cents off the cost.

2. A good _____ is short and easy to remember.

3. People _____ to get new customers.

4. The company sent us a free _____ of dog food.

5. The drivers smiled when they saw the new _____.

Consonant Clusters

Game Plan

Three consonants together in a word make a **consonant cluster.** In many List Words, **s** forms a cluster with two other letters. In some List Words, /ch/ or /th/ forms a cluster with another letter.

List Words

1. splash
2. spring
3. patch
4. strong
5. thrills
6. spray
7. scream
8. throw
9. string
10. struck
11. screen
12. itch
13. pitch
14. spread
15. strawberry
16. stream
17. split
18. scratch
19. ditch
20. thread

Warm Up

Finish each List Word by writing a consonant cluster.

1. _____ ash
2. _____ ead
3. _____ ing
4. _____ ong
5. _____ it
6. _____ awberry
7. _____ ead
8. _____ ills
9. _____ ing
10. _____ ow

11. pi _____
12. pa _____
13. _____ atch
14. _____ uck
15. di _____
16. i _____
17. _____ eam
18. _____ ay
19. _____ een
20. _____ eam

They **spray** the **strawberry patch.**

117

Practice

Alphabetical Order

Write each group of List Words in
alphabetical order.

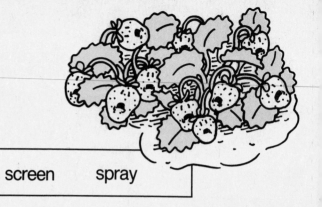

| spring | splash | spread | split | screen | spray |

1. _____   3. _____   5. _____

2. _____   4. _____   6. _____

| struck | scratch | string | scream | steam | strong |

7. _____   9. _____   11. _____

8. _____   10. _____   12. _____

Puzzle

Write a List Word to solve each clue. Then read
down the shaded boxes to answer the riddle.

1. This word names a fruit.

2. This will keep flies out of your home.

3. This is a loud yell.

4. This means "hit."

5. This word names a deep hole.

RIDDLE: What did the strawberry patch say to the rain?

ANSWER: If you keep this up, my name will ___ ___ ___ ___ ___ !

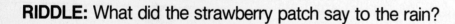

List Words

splash	spray	screen	stream
spring	scream	itch	split
patch	throw	pitch	scratch
strong	string	spread	ditch
thrills	struck	strawberry	thread

Classification

Write the List Word that belongs in each group.

1. orange, apple, _____

2. yell, shout, _____

3. fall, winter, _____

4. share, divide, _____

5. throw, toss, _____

6. joy, excitement, _____

7. string, ribbon, _____

8. brook, river, _____

9. hole, pit, _____

10. hit, slapped, _____

Rhyming

Write one or more List Words to rhyme with the words given.

1. witch _____

_____

_____

2. day _____

3. red _____

_____

4. know _____

5. wrong _____

6. truck _____

7. cream _____

_____

8. hills _____

9. match _____

10. mash _____

11. bean _____

12. ring _____

119

Challenges

Reading and Writing

Unscratchable Itch

There is a spot that you can't scratch
Right between your shoulder blades,
Like an egg that just won't hatch
Here you set and there it stays.
Turn and squirm and try to reach it,
Twist your neck and bend your back,
Hear your elbows creak and crack,

Stretch your fingers, now you bet it's
Going to reach—no that won't get it—
Hold your breath and stretch and pray,
Only just an inch away,
Worse than a sunbeam you can't catch
Is that one spot that
You can't scratch.

—Shel Silverstein

From A LIGHT IN THE ATTIC: The Poems and Drawings of Shel Silverstein: "Unscratchable Itch" copyright © 1981 by Evil Eye Music, Inc.

Write this man a note. Suggest a way for him to reach and scratch that "unscratchable itch."

Bonus Words: Itches

rash   poison ivy   poison oak   allergy   ointment

Write Bonus Words to answer the questions. Use each word only once.

1. What plants may make you itch? _____

_____

2. What do we call a red, bumpy, itchy place on the skin? _____

3. What may help that red, bumpy, itchy place? _____

4. What condition may cause a person to get a rash? _____

Game Plan

Vowel sounds are spelled in different ways. Listen for the /ô/ sound in <u>flaw</u>, <u>because</u>, <u>wallet</u>, <u>cost</u>, and <u>bought</u>. How is the sound spelled in each word? Now listen for the /oi/ sound in <u>join</u> and <u>toy</u>, and for the /ou/ sound in <u>loud</u> and <u>town</u>. Each sound can be spelled more than one way.

Two consonants can join together in a word to make a **consonant digraph.** Listen for the digraph sounds in <u>thaw</u>, <u>then</u>, <u>short</u>, <u>check</u>, <u>whale</u>, and <u>who</u>. Three consonants can join together to form a **cluster**. Listen for the consonant clusters in <u>spring</u>, <u>itch</u>, and <u>thrills</u>.

Practice

Write a List Word that matches each clue.

Lesson 25	
almost	wallet
laws	all right
August	crawl

1. summer month
_____

2. rules
_____

3. not quite
_____

4. to creep
_____

5. money holder
_____

6. good enough
_____

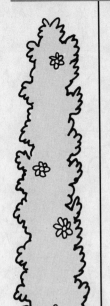

Write each List Word under the number of syllables it contains.

I

1. _____

2. _____

3. _____

2

4. _____

5. _____

6. _____

Lesson **26**

crowd	power
point	choice
about	loyal

_____

_____

Write a List Word that rhymes with each word given.

Lesson **27**

fourth	thinking
push	that
thumb	shine

_____

_____

1. mine

_____

2. hum

_____

3. flat

4. north

_____

5. bush

_____

6. sinking

_____

Write the List Words in alphabetical order.

1. _____   4. _____

2. _____   5. _____

3. _____   6. _____

Lesson **28**

which	catch
check	whisper
chart	whole

_____

_____

Read the first two underlined words in each sentence. Write the List Word that goes with the third underlined word in the same way.

1. <u>Big</u> is to <u>large</u> as <u>yell</u> is to

   _____.

2. <u>Cut</u> is to <u>scissors</u> as <u>sew</u> is to

   _____.

3. <u>Up</u> is to <u>down</u> as <u>catch</u> is to

   _____.

4. <u>On</u> is to <u>off</u> as <u>weak</u> is to

   _____.

5. <u>Winter</u> is to <u>summer</u> as <u>fall</u> is to

   _____.

6. <u>Road</u> is to <u>street</u> as <u>creek</u> is to

   _____.

Lesson **29**

spring	strong
scream	throw
stream	thread

_____

_____

almost	crowd
shine	point
fourth	thumb
whisper	which
loyal	thread

Mixed Practice

Fill in the crossword puzzle by writing a List Word to answer each clue.

ACROSS

1. faithful
5. talk quietly
6. sounds like <u>witch</u>
9. a very fine string
10. a sharp end

DOWN

2. not completely
3. comes after the third
4. one of ten fingers
7. large number of people
8. to gleam or glow

Consonant Digraphs

Game Plan

The /n/ can be spelled with **kn** or **gn** as in know and sign. The /r/ can be spelled with **wr** as in wrote. The /f/ can be spelled with **gh** or **ph** as in phone and rough. The /k/ can be spelled with **ch** or **ck** as in school and wreck.

List Words

1. school
2. wrote
3. phone
4. knew
5. sign
6. knots
7. wrong
8. knee
9. knife
10. wreck
11. wrap
12. knock
13. rough
14. laugh
15. elephant
16. cough
17. wren
18. writer
19. graph
20. track

Warm Up

Say each sound. Write the List Words that spell that sound with a digraph. Then circle the digraph in each word. Some words will be used more than once.

/n/

1. _____
2. _____
3. _____
4. _____
5. _____
6. _____

/r/

7. _____
8. _____
9. _____
10. _____
11. _____
12. _____

/f/

13. _____
14. _____
15. _____
16. _____
17. _____
18. _____

/k/

19. _____
20. _____
21. _____
22. _____

125

Practice

Puzzle

Fill in the crossword puzzle by writing a List Word
to answer each clue.

ACROSS
1. not correct
3. felt sure about
4. message on a board
6. something that is a mess
9. a place to learn
10. an animal footprint

DOWN
1. a small bird
2. a chart
3. the bend in your leg
5. rap on a door
6. used a pen
   and paper
7. made when
   rope is tied
8. to put a cover around

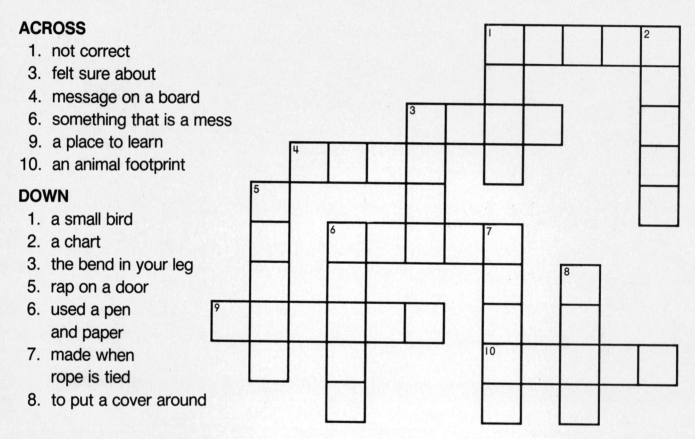

Missing Words

Write a List Word from the box to finish
each phrase.

knots	cough	knife	elephant	rough	laugh

1. sharp as a _____

2. as _____ as sandpaper

3. as big as an _____

4. _____ it up

5. the last _____

6. all tied up in _____

List Words

school	knots	wrap	cough
wrote	wrong	knock	wren
phone	knee	rough	writer
knew	knife	laugh	graph
sign	wreck	elephant	track

Misspelled Words

In each set of List Words one is misspelled. Circle the word that is wrong. Write it correctly on the line.

1. school   sign   righter   _____

2. ren   knew   cough   _____

3. knots   elefant   track   _____

4. nee   wrote   phone   _____

5. knife   laff   rough   _____

6. sine   knock   wrap   _____

7. writer   rong   elephant   _____

8. graph   wren   skool   _____

9. ruf   knee   wreck   _____

10. wrote   niffe   rough   _____

Rhyming

Write List Words that rhyme with the words given.

1. block _____   4. trap _____

2. pots _____   5. fluff _____

3. lighter _____   6. tone _____

Challenges

Reading and Writing

Snored and Snored

An elephant lay in his bunk
In slumber his chest rose and sunk.
  He snored and he snored,
    Till the jungle folks roared—
And his wife tied a knot in his trunk.

—Limerick

A **limerick** is a five line rhyming poem that tells a silly story. Write a limerick about a zoo animal. You might write about a giraffe and its long neck, a monkey and its curly tail, or any other animal you choose.

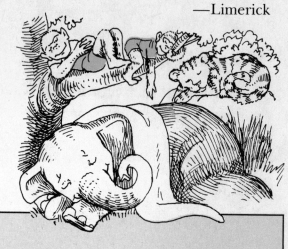

Bonus Words: Places to Sleep

bunk   cot   crib   hammock   water bed

Write the Bonus Word that matches the picture clue.

  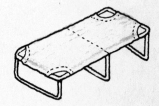

1. _____   2. _____   3. _____

4. _____   5. _____

Game Plan

A **prefix** is a word part added to the beginning of a **root word**. It changes the root's meaning, as in <u>unseen</u> or <u>dislike</u>.

The prefixes **dis** and **un** can make a root mean <u>the opposite</u>. The prefix **un** can also mean <u>not</u>. Think about the meaning of each List Word.

List Words

1. unseen
2. unable
3. discover
4. unload
5. unclean
6. unsure
7. uneven
8. dislike
9. displease
10. distrust
11. unwrap
12. untrue
13. unlucky
14. unchanged
15. untouched
16. disobey
17. disorder
18. unbutton
19. unpaid
20. disappear

Warm Up

Write each List Word under its prefix.

dis

1. _____   5. _____

2. _____   6. _____

3. _____   7. _____

4. _____

un

8. _____   15. _____

9. _____   16. _____

10. _____   17. _____

11. _____   18. _____

12. _____   19. _____

13. _____   20. _____

14. _____

clean   **unclean**

129

Practice

Synonyms

Write the List Word that means the same as the word given.

1. find _____   **4.** hidden _____

2. false _____   **5.** hate _____

3. mess _____   **6.** dirty _____

Antonyms

Write the List Word that means the opposite of the word given.

1. believe _____   **3.** handled _____

2. satisfy _____   **4.** fortunate _____

Scrambled Letters

Unscramble the letters to spell each root word. Write the List Word that contains it.

1. bale _____   **5.** boye _____

2. aldo _____   **6.** neev _____

3. praw _____   **7.** reus _____

4. hangced _____   **8.** tunobt _____

List Words

unseen	unsure	unwrap	disobey
unable	uneven	untrue	disorder
discover	dislike	unlucky	unbutton
unload	displease	unchanged	unpaid
unclean	distrust	untouched	disappear

Comparing Words

Read the first two underlined words in each sentence. Write the List Word that goes with the third word in the same way.

1. Four-leaf clover is to lucky as black cat is to _____.

2. Zipper is to unzip as button is to _____.

3. On is to off as true is to _____.

Word Shape Puzzle

Write a List Word in each word shape.

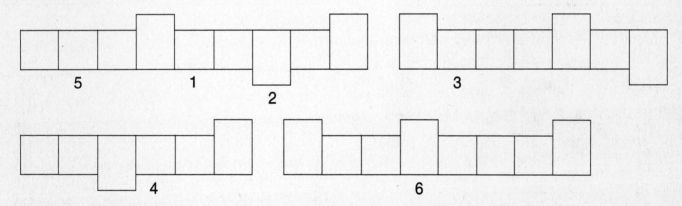

Use the number code to answer the riddle. Find the letter in the box with the number 1 under it. Print that letter on the line with the same number. Do the same for numbers 2 through 6.

RIDDLE: What is the largest ant?   **ANSWER:** ____ ____ ____ ____ ____ ____
                                                      1   2   3   4   5   6

Challenges

Reading and Writing

Me a Mess?

Unclean and unbuckled,
Unfastened, untied,
Unfit to be seen,
I'm undignified.
Unfolded, unbuttoned,
Unbecoming, no less.
Unfortunately I'm
Unaware I'm a mess.

—Babs Bell Hajdusiewicz

Write a poem about someone who is the opposite
of a mess.

Bonus Words: Clothes

    suit   jacket   jeans   pants   vest

Write the Bonus Word that names each item.

1. _____   2. _____   4. _____

3. _____   5. _____

Game Plan

The prefix **re** can mean <u>again</u> or <u>back</u>.
re + **tell** = <u>retell</u>, meaning "tell again"
re + **pay** = <u>repay</u>, meaning "pay back"
Think about the meaning of **re** in each of
the List Words.

List Words

1. rename
2. remind
3. refresh
4. retell
5. rewrite
6. replay
7. repay
8. refill
9. reload
10. rerun
11. replace
12. redo
13. replant
14. renew
15. rebuild
16. recopy
17. regroup
18. rethink
19. rework
20. reform

Warm Up

Add the prefix **re** to each of these roots to form a
List Word. Write the List Words.

1. form _____
2. build _____
3. load _____
4. mind _____
5. place _____
6. think _____
7. group _____
8. plant _____
9. write _____
10. fresh _____

11. copy _____
12. do _____
13. tell _____
14. new _____
15. pay _____
16. fill _____
17. run _____
18. work _____
19. play _____
20. name _____

He will **replant,** and she will **refill.**

133

Practice

Definitions

Write the List Word that matches the meaning given.

re = back
re = again

1. to build again _____

2. to pay back _____

3. to give a new name to _____

4. to bring a thought back to someone's mind _____

5. to write again, especially to make corrections _____

6. to get people back together again _____

7. to provide information again _____

8. to think about something in a new way _____

Puzzle

Fill in the crossword puzzle by unscrambling each set of letters to write a List Word.

ACROSS
3. RETWIRE
6. RECLEAP
7. YAPER

DOWN
1. GROPURE
2. SHREEFR
3. PRAYLE
4. PORCEY
5. KREROW

List Words

rename	replay	replace	recopy
remind	repay	redo	regroup
refresh	refill	replant	rethink
retell	reload	renew	rework
rewrite	rerun	rebuild	reform

Rhyming

The root of a List Word rhymes with each of these words. Write the complete List Word.

1. can't _____

2. floppy _____

3. sun _____

4. ink _____

5. face _____

6. blue _____

7. toad _____

8. warm _____

9. flight _____

10. loop _____

11. hill _____

12. kind _____

Missing Words

Write a List Word to finish each sentence.

1. Since "Brownie" is so common, I'll _____ my dog "Buttons."

2. We have to _____ the rose bush in a larger pot.

3. The farmer will _____ his ruined barn.

4. A cold glass of lemonade will _____ the tired hiker.

5. Sarah will use wallpaper to _____ the walls of her room.

6. Please _____ the math problem to find your mistake.

7. Please _____ that funny joke you told me yesterday.

8. Listen as I _____ the record a final time.

Challenges

Reading and Writing

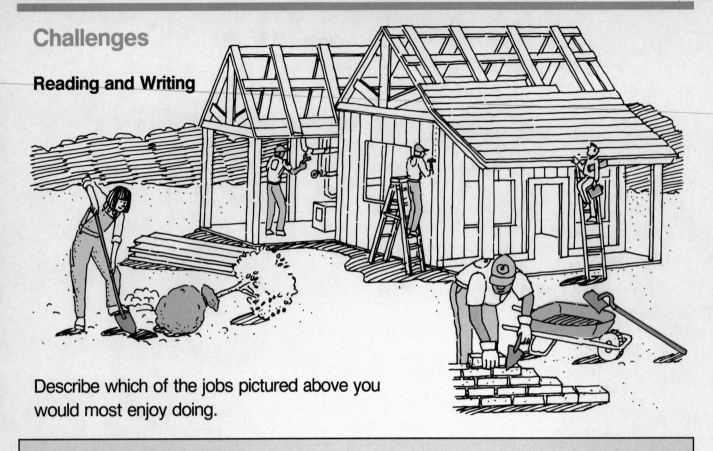

Describe which of the jobs pictured above you would most enjoy doing.

Bonus Words: Jobs

   carpenter   plumber   gardener   builder   bricklayer

Write a Bonus Word as a caption to each picture.

1. _____   2. _____   3. _____

4. _____   5. _____

Contractions

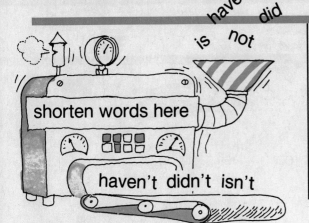

shorten words here

haven't didn't isn't

Game Plan

All the List Words are **contractions,** or short ways to write two words. He's is a contraction for <u>he is.</u> I'd is a contraction for <u>I would.</u> The **apostrophe** (') shows where letters are left out.

Warm Up

Use the word given and the word at the top of each set to spell your List Words. Write the contractions on the lines.

List Words		**not**		**is**
1. there's		1. have _____		12. there _____
2. haven't		2. could _____		13. he _____
3. he's		3. is _____		14. that _____
4. couldn't		4. did _____		**will**
5. that's		5. must _____		15. I _____
6. I'll		6. should _____		16. we _____
7. isn't		7. was _____		**are**
8. didn't		8. will _____		17. they _____
9. they're		9. would _____		**would**
10. we'll		10. do _____		18. I _____
11. mustn't		11. does _____		**have**
12. shouldn't				19. I _____
13. wasn't				20. you _____
14. won't				
15. I'd				
16. wouldn't				
17. don't				
18. I've				
19. you've				
20. doesn't				

Practice

Contractions

Circle the two words in each sentence that can be shortened into a contraction. Write the contraction List Words.

1. You must not tell my secret.

_____

2. We have not seen Bill all day.

_____

3. Pedro is not feeling well.

_____

4. You have made me happy.

_____

Alphabetical Order

Write each group of List Words in alphabetical order.

doesn't didn't don't

we'll won't wasn't

1. _____

2. _____

3. _____

4. _____

5. _____

6. _____

Proofreading

Each sentence has two mistakes. Use the proofreading marks to fix each mistake. Write each sentence correctly on the line.

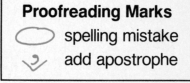

Proofreading Marks

⟳ spelling mistake

˯ add apostrophe

1. I ve fed the dog, so you shoudn't.

_____

2. Hee's on his way and won t be late.

_____

List Words

there's	I'll	mustn't	wouldn't
haven't	isn't	shouldn't	don't
he's	didn't	wasn't	I've
couldn't	they're	won't	you've
that's	we'll	I'd	doesn't

Rhyming

Write List Words that rhyme with the words given. Don't forget to use apostrophes.

1. bears _____   **3.** smile _____   **5.** hide _____

2. hive _____   **4.** bats _____   **6.** hair _____

Write three List Words that rhyme with each other.

7. _____   **8.** _____   **9.** _____

Missing Words

Write List Words to finish the letter. Write the contractions on the numbered lines.

Dear Betty,

    Thank you for inviting us to spend a week at your house this summer. My sisters __1__ be able to come along. __2__ going to summer school this year.

    __3__ always so much to do at your house. __4__ be sure to bring my swimsuit. I __5__ able to swim at all last year. __6__ swim like fish this Saturday!

    It __7__ take us long to get there. It will be fun to see you again. __8__ the best part of all!

Sincerely,
Melanie

1. _____
2. _____
3. _____
4. _____
5. _____
6. _____
7. _____
8. _____

Challenges

Reading and Writing

If We Didn't Have Birthdays

If we didn't have birthdays, you wouldn't be you.
If you'd never been born, well then what would you do?
If you'd never been born, well then what would you be?
You *might* be a fish! Or a toad in a tree!
You might be a doorknob! Or three baked potatoes!
You might be a bag full of hard green tomatoes.
Or worse than all that . . . Why, you might be a WASN'T!
A Wasn't has no fun at all. No, he doesn't.
A Wasn't just isn't. He just isn't present.
But you . . . You ARE YOU! And, now isn't that pleasant!

—Dr. Seuss

Write about what you would be if you weren't a person. What would you look like? Where would you live? How would you have fun? Who would be your friends?

Bonus Words: Pronouns

myself   himself   herself   yourself   ourselves

Write the Bonus Word that completes each sentence.

1. Jane looked in the mirror and drew a picture of _____.

2. I made _____ a sandwich for lunch.

3. We kept _____ busy cleaning up our rooms.

4. Stan built this treehouse all by _____.

5. Be careful with that sharp knife or you will cut _____.

Homonyms

Game Plan

Homonyms are words that sound alike but have different meanings and different spellings. The words <u>two</u>, <u>to</u>, and <u>too</u> are homonyms. Find the pairs or groups of homonyms as you read the List Words.

List Words

1. hear
2. here
3. tied
4. tide
5. your
6. you're
7. hour
8. our
9. sail
10. sale
11. two
12. to
13. too
14. pair
15. pear
16. pare
17. maid
18. made
19. great
20. grate

Warm Up

Write the List Words that contain the vowel sounds given.

/ā/ as in <u>say</u>

1. _____
2. _____
3. _____
4. _____
5. _____
6. _____

/ir/ as in <u>year</u>

7. _____
8. _____

/ōo/ as in <u>food</u>

9. _____
10. _____
11. _____

/er/ as in <u>care</u>

12. _____
13. _____
14. _____

/ôr/ as in <u>for</u>

15. _____
16. _____

/ī/ as in <u>side</u>

17. _____
18. _____

/ou/ as in <u>found</u>

19. _____
20. _____

Practice

Definitions

Write the List Word that matches the meaning given.

1. also _____
2. cut or trim _____
3. your and my _____
4. a sea change _____
5. knotted _____
6. use ears _____
7. boat part _____
8. a fruit _____
9. not my _____
10. metal frame _____

11. in this place _____
12. big _____
13. sixty minutes _____
14. a set _____
15. low prices _____
16. a contraction _____
17. house cleaner _____
18. a number _____
19. toward _____
20. built _____

Homonyms

Write two List Words that are homonyms to answer each riddle.

1. What did the boy say when he saw the fireplace grill?

   What a _____ _____!

2. What did the girl ask the cook to do?

   Please _____ the skin off this _____.

3. What happened to the messy bed in the hotel room?

   The _____ _____ it.

4. What did the people sitting at the concert say?

   We can really _____ well _____.

List Words

hear	you're	two	pare
here	hour	to	maid
tied	our	too	made
tide	sail	pair	great
your	sale	pear	grate

Scrambled Letters

Unscramble the letters to make List Words.

1. tdei

___ ___ ___ ___

___ ___ ___ ___

2. retga

___ ___ ___ ___ ___

___ ___ ___ ___ ___

Double one letter to make a new word. Write the word.

3. to

___ ___ ___ ___

Add a letter to make a new word. Write the word.

4. our

___ ___ ___ ___

Comparing Words

Read the first two underlined words in each sentence. Write the List Word that goes with the third word in the same way.

1. <u>One</u> is to <u>two</u> as <u>single</u> is to _____.

2. <u>Second</u> is to <u>minute</u> as <u>minute</u> is to _____.

3. <u>Eye</u> is to <u>see</u> as <u>ear</u> is to _____.

4. <u>Car</u> is to <u>drive</u> as <u>boat</u> is to _____.

5. <u>Fingers</u> is to <u>ten</u> as <u>hands</u> is to _____.

Challenges

Reading and Writing

<h2 style="text-align:center">On the Bridge</h2>

If I could see a little fish—
That is what I just now wish!
I want to see his great round eyes
Always open in surprise.

I wish a water-rat would glide
Slowly to the other side;
Or a dancing spider sit
On the yellow flags a bit.

I think I'll get some stones to throw,
And watch the pretty circles show.
Or shall we sail a flower boat,
And watch it slowly—slowly float?

That's nice—because you never know
How far away it means to go;
And when tomorrow comes, you see,
It may be in the great wide sea.

—Kate Greenaway

Write a description that tells what you might see
if you were on the bridge? What would you
like to see?

Bonus Words: Rivers

Mississippi   Rio Grande   Colorado   Ohio   Columbia

Write the Bonus Word that names each river.

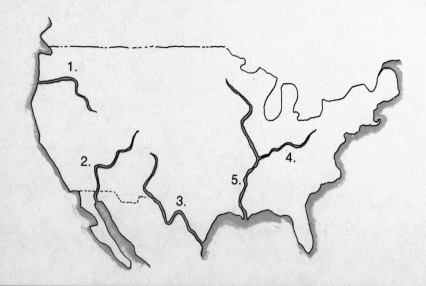

1. _____

2. _____

3. _____

4. _____

5. _____

Game Plan

A **consonant digraph** is consonants together that make one sound. Listen for the consonant digraph in knot, <u>wrong</u>, <u>rough</u>, <u>phone</u>. A **prefix** is a word part that is added to the beginning of a **root word,** as in <u>unable</u>, <u>discover</u>, <u>retell</u>, and <u>redo</u>.

A **contraction** is a word made by writing two words together and leaving out one or more letters. An apostrophe shows where letters are missing, as in <u>I'll</u>. **Homonyms** are words that sound alike, but have different meanings and spellings, such as <u>sale</u> and <u>sail</u>.

Practice

Write a List Word that means the opposite of each word given.

Lesson 31	
knew	wrong
wreck	wrap
rough	laugh

_____

_____

1. fix _____

2. right _____

3. forgot _____

4. smooth _____

5. unwrap _____

6. cry _____

Write each List Word under the number of syllables it contains.

Lesson **32**

disobey	unclean
untrue	displease
unbutton	unlucky

_____

_____

2 Syllables

1. _____

2. _____

3. _____

3 Syllables

4. _____

5. _____

6. _____

Look at each set of guide words. Decide which List Words go between each set. Then write them in alphabetical order.

Lesson **33**

rename	reform
redo	refill
replace	renew

_____

_____

rebuild - regroup

1. _____

2. _____

3. _____

remind - replant

4. _____

5. _____

6. _____

Write a List Word that rhymes with each word given.

1. wasn't

_____

2. bears

_____

3. hair

_____

4. wide

_____

5. bees

_____

6. wouldn't

_____

Lesson **34**

there's	he's
couldn't	they're
doesn't	I'd

_____

_____

Write a List Word to complete each sentence.

Lesson **35**

your	you're
to	too
here	hear

_____

1. When you whisper, I can't _____.

2. Each person must walk _____ the exit.

3. It is getting _____ dark to read.

4. Please hang _____ coat in the hall.

5. We will be _____ when you return.

6. I see that _____ on my bus now.

knew	wreck
rough	disobey
unbutton	refill
reform	there's
couldn't	hear
redo	you're

Mixed Practice

In each set of List Words, one word is misspelled. Circle the List Word that is wrong. Then write it correctly on the line.

1. unbutton   you're   disobay   _____

2. redoo   rough   refill   _____

3. reform   wreck   knoo   _____

4. your'e   couldn't   there's   _____

5. knew   reck   hear   _____

6. couldn't   reform   ther'es   _____

7. redo   refil   rough   _____

8. unbuton   disobey   refill   _____

9. redo   knew   heer   _____

10. wreck   rouph   you're   _____

11. disobey   refform   unbutton   _____

12. there's   you're   coudn't   _____

Writing and Proofreading Guide

1. Choose a topic to write about.

2. Write your ideas. Don't worry about mistakes.

3. Now organize your writing so that it makes sense.

4. Proofread your work.

Use these proofreading marks to make changes.

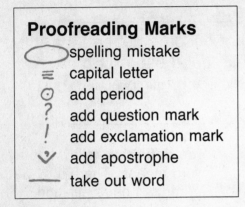

Proofreading Marks
- ⬭ spelling mistake
- ≡ capital letter
- ⊙ add period
- ? add question mark
- ! add exclamation mark
- ⌄ add apostrophe
- —— take out word

i̱t̲s time for the ~~the~~ cool ⬭goos⬭ to read a book⊙

5. Write your final copy.

It's time for the cool goose to read a book.

Using Your Dictionary

The Spelling Workout Dictionary shows you many things about your spelling words.

The **respelling** tells how to pronounce the word.

The **entry word** listed in alphabetical order is the word you are looking up.

The **part of speech** is given as an abbreviation.

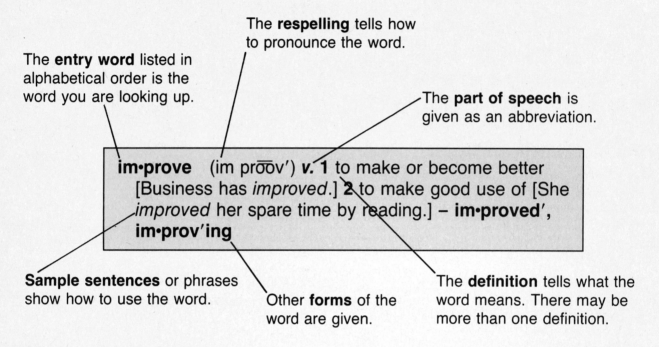

im·prove (im prōōv′) *v.* **1** to make or become better [Business has *improved*.] **2** to make good use of [She *improved* her spare time by reading.] – **im·proved′, im·prov′ing**

Sample sentences or phrases show how to use the word.

Other **forms** of the word are given.

The **definition** tells what the word means. There may be more than one definition.

Pronunciation Key

SYMBOL	KEY WORDS	SYMBOL	KEY WORDS	SYMBOL	KEY WORDS	SYMBOL	KEY WORDS
a	ask, fat	ळ	look, pull	b	bed, dub	w	will, always
ā	ape, date	ळ̄	ooze, tool	d	did, had	y	yet, yard
ä	car, lot			f	fall, off	z	zebra, haze
		yळ	unite, cure	g	get, dog		
e	elf, ten	yळ̄	cute, few	h	he, ahead	ch	chin, arch
er	berry, care	ळu	out, crowd	j	joy, jump	ng	ring, singer
ē	even, meet	u	up, cut	k	kill, bake	sh	she, dash
		ur	fur, fern	l	let, ball	th	thin, truth
i	is, hit			m	met, trim	*th*	then, father
ir	mirror, here	ə	a in ago	n	not, ton	zh	s in pleasure
ī	ice, fire		e in agent	p	put, tap		
			e in father	r	red, dear	′	as in (ā′b′l)
ō	open, go		i in unity	s	sell, pass		
ô	law, horn		o in collect	t	top, hat		
oi	oil, point		u in focus	v	vat, have		

An Americanism is a word or usage of a word that was born in this country. An open star before an entry word or definition means that the word or definition is an Americanism.

These dictionary entries are taken, by permission, in abridged or modified form from *Webster's New World Dictionary for Young Readers*. Copyright © 1989 by Simon & Schuster, Inc.

Aa

a·bout (ə bout′) **adv.** **1** on every side; all around [Look *about*.] **2** nearly; more or less [*about* ten years old]. ◆**adj.** active; awake or recovered [At dawn I was up and *about*.] ◆**prep.** **1** almost ready [I am *about* to cry.] **2** having to do with [a book *about* ships].

ac·ro·bat (ak′rə bat) **n.** a performer who does tricks in tumbling or on the trapeze, tightrope, etc.

a·cross (ə krôs′) **adv.** from one side to the other [The new bridge makes it easy to get *across* in a car.] ◆**prep.** **1** from one side to the other of [We swam *across* the river.] **2** on the other side of [They live *across* the street.]

act (akt) **n.** **1** a thing done; deed [an *act* of bravery]. **2** one of the main divisions of a play, opera, etc. [The first *act* takes place in a palace.] ◆**v.** **1** to play the part of, as on a stage [She *acted* Juliet.] **2** to behave like [Don't *act* the fool.]

add (ad) **v.** **1** to put or join something to another thing so that there will be more or so as to mix into one thing [We *added* some books to our library. *Add* two cups of sugar to the batter.] **2** to join numbers so as to get a total, or sum [*Add* 3 and 5.]

ad·mit (əd mit′) **v.** **1** to permit or give the right to enter [One ticket *admits* two persons.] **2** to take or accept as being true; confess [Lucy will not *admit* her mistake.] —**ad·mit′ted, ad·mit′ting**

ad·ver·tise (ad′vər tīz) **v.** **1** to tell about a product in public and in such a way as to make people want to buy it [to *advertise* cars on television]. **2** to announce or ask for publicly, as in a newspaper [to *advertise* a house for rent; to *advertise* for a cook]. —**ad′ver·tised, ad′ver·tis·ing** —**ad′ver·tis′er** **n.**

af·ter·noon (af tər nōon′) **n.** the time of day from noon to evening.

a·gain (ə gen′) **adv.** once more; a second time [If you don't understand the sentence, read it *again*.]

age (āj) **n.** **1** the time that a person or thing has existed from birth or beginning [He left school at the *age* of fourteen.] **2** the fact of being old [Gray hair comes with *age*.]

A·las·ka (ə las′kə) a state of the U.S. in northwestern North America, separated from Asia by the Bering Strait: abbreviated **Alas., AK** —**A·las′kan adj., n.**

al·ien (āl′yən) **n.** **1** a foreigner. **2** a person living in a country but not a citizen of it. **3** an imaginary being from outer space, as in science fiction, that visits the earth.

a·live (ə līv′) **adj.** **1** having life; living. **2** going on; in action; not ended or destroyed [to keep old memories *alive*]. **3** lively; alert.

☆**al·ler·gy** (al′ər jē) **n.** a condition in which one becomes sick, gets a rash, etc., by breathing in, touching, eating, or drinking something that is not harmful to most people [Hay fever is usually caused by an *allergy* to certain pollens.] —*pl.* **al′ler·gies**

al·low (ə lou′) **v.** **1** to let be done; permit; let [*Allow* us to pay. No smoking *allowed*.] **2** to give or keep an extra amount so as to have enough [*Allow* an inch for shrinkage.]

all right **1** good enough; satisfactory; adequate [Your work is *all right*.] **2** yes; very well [*All right*, I'll do it.]

acrobat

151

al·most (ôl′mōst) *adv.* not completely but very nearly [He tripped and *almost* fell. Sue is *almost* ten.]

al·read·y (ôl red′ē) *adv.* **1** by or before this time [When we arrived, dinner had *already* begun.] **2** even now [I am *already* ten minutes late.]

al·ways (ôl′wiz *or* ôl′wāz) *adv.* at all times; at every time [*Always* be courteous.]

an·gry (aŋ′grē) *adj.* **1** feeling or showing anger [*angry* words; an *angry* crowd]. **2** wild and stormy [an *angry* sea]. —**an′gri·er, an′gri·est**

an·y (en′ē) *adj.* **1** one, no matter which one, of more than two [*Any* pupil may answer.] **2** some, no matter how much, how many, or what kind [Do you have *any* apples?] ◆*pron.* any one or ones; any amount or number [I lost my pencils; do you have *any*?]

an·y·one (en′ē wun) *pron.* any person; anybody [Does *anyone* know where the house is?]

an·y·way (en′ē wā) *adv.* nevertheless; anyhow.

ap·pear (ə pir′) *v.* to come into sight or into being [A ship *appeared* on the horizon. Leaves *appear* on the tree every spring.]

a·rith·me·tic (ə rith′mə tik) *n.* the science or art of using numbers, especially in adding, subtracting, multiplying, and dividing. —**ar·ith·met·i·cal** (ar′ith met′i k′l) *adj.*

ar·my (är′mē) *n.* **1** a large group of soldiers trained for war, especially on land; also, all the soldiers of a country. **2** any large group of persons or animals [An *army* of workers was building the bridge.] —*pl.* **ar′mies**

At·lan·ta (ət lan′tə) the capital of Georgia, in the northern part.

Au·gust (ô′gəst) *n.* the eighth month of the year, which has 31 days: abbreviated **Aug.**

aw·ful (ô′fəl) *adj.* **1** making one feel awe or dread; causing fear [an *awful* scene of destruction]. **2** very bad, ugly, great, etc.: *used only in everyday talk* [an *awful* joke; an *awful* fool].

Atlanta

ba·by (bā′bē) *n.* **1** a very young child; infant. **2** a person who seems helpless, cries easily, etc., like a baby. **3** the youngest or smallest in a group. —*pl.* **ba′bies**

bank[1] (baŋk) *n.* a place of business for keeping, exchanging, or lending money. Banks make a profit by charging interest for the money they lend.

bank[2] (baŋk) *n.* the land along the sides of a river or stream. ◆*v.* to pile up so as to form a bank [The snow was *banked* along the driveway.]

base·ment (bās′mənt) *n.* the cellar or lowest rooms of a building, below the main floor and at least partly below the surface of the ground.

be (bē) *v.* *Be* is used to join a subject with a word or words that tell something about it. It is also used to tell that something exists or takes place, and as a helping verb with other verb forms. **1** *Be* may join a subject with a noun, adjective, or pronoun [Ed and Lois *are* students. Mary *is* tall. Who *is* he?] **2** *Be* may mean "to live," "to happen or take place," or "to stay or continue" [Lincoln *is* no more. The wedding will *be* next Saturday. I will *be* here until Monday.] —**was** *or* **were, been, be′ing**

be·cause (bi kôz′) *conj.* for the reason that; since [I'm late *because* I overslept.]

bed·room (bed′rōōm) *n.* a room with a bed, for sleeping in.

bees·wax (bēz′waks) *n.* the wax that some bees make for building their honeycomb. It is used in making candles and polishes.

be·fore (bi fôr´) *prep.* earlier than; previous to [Will you finish *before* noon?] ◆*adv.* in the past; earlier [I've heard that song *before.*] ◆*conj.* earlier than the time that [Think *before* you speak.]

be·gin·ning (bi gin´iŋ) *n.* a start or starting; first part or first action [We came in just after the *beginning* of the movie. Going to the dance together was the *beginning* of our friendship.]

be·long (bi lôŋ´) *v.* **1** to have its proper place [This chair *belongs* in the corner.] **2** to be owned by someone [This book *belongs* to you.]

be·low (bi lō´) *adv., adj.* in or to a lower place; beneath [I'll take the upper bunk and you can sleep *below.*] ◆*prep.* lower than in place, position, price, rank, etc. [the people living *below* us; a price *below* $25].

bench (bench) *n.* a long, hard seat for several persons, with or without a back.

ber·ry (ber´ē) *n.* any small, juicy fruit with seeds and a soft pulp, as a strawberry, blackberry, or blueberry. In scientific use, many fleshy fruits having a skin are classed as berries, for example, the tomato, banana, and grape. —*pl.* **ber´ries**

be·side (bi sīd´) *prep.* by or at the side of; close to [The garage is *beside* the house.]

best (best) *adj.* above all others in worth or ability; most excellent, most fit, most desirable, etc. [Joan is the *best* player on the team. When is the *best* time to plant tulips?] ◆*adv.* **1** in a way that is best or most excellent, fit, etc. [Which choir sang *best*?] **2** more than any other; most [Of all your books, I like that one *best.*] ◆*n.* **1** a person or thing that is most excellent, most fit, etc. [That doctor is among the *best* in

the profession. When I buy shoes, I buy the *best.*] **2** the most that can be done; utmost [We did our *best* to win.]

bet·ter (bet´ər) *adj.* **1** above another, as in worth or ability; more excellent, more fit, more desirable, etc. [Grace is a *better* player than Chris. I have a *better* idea.] **2** not so sick; more healthy than before. ◆*adv.* **1** in a way that is better or more excellent, fit, etc. [They will sing *better* with more practice.] **2** more [I like the orange drink *better* than the lime.]

big (big) *adj.* of great size; large [a *big* cake; a *big* city]. —**big´ger, big´gest** —**big´ness** *n.*

☆**bill·board** (bil´bôrd) *n.* a large board outdoors, on which advertisements are posted.

bird (burd) *n.* a warmblooded animal that has a backbone, two feet, and wings, and is covered with feathers. Birds lay eggs and can usually fly.

blame (blām) *v.* to say or think that someone or something is the cause of what is wrong or bad [Don't *blame* others for your own mistakes.] —**blamed, blam´ing** ◆*n.* the fact of being the cause of what is wrong or bad [I will take the *blame* for the broken window.]

blaze (blāz) *n.* a bright flame or fire. ◆*v.* to burn brightly. —**blazed, blaz´ing**

blind (blīnd) *adj.* not able to see; having no sight. ◆*v.* to make blind; make unable to see. ◆*n.* a window shade of stiffened cloth, metal slats, etc.

blood (blud) *n.* the red liquid that is pumped through the arteries and veins by the heart. The blood carries oxygen and cell-building material to the body tissues and carries carbon dioxide and waste material away from them.

billboard

a	ask, fat
ā	ape, date
ä	car, lot
e	elf, ten
er	berry, care
ē	even, meet
i	is, hit
ir	mirror, here
ī	ice, fire
ō	open, go
ô	law, horn
oi	oil, point
oo	look, pull
ōō	ooze, tool
yoo	unite, cure
yōō	cute, few
ou	out, crowd
u	up, cut
ur	fur, fern
ə	a in ago
	e in agent
	e in father
	i in unity
	o in collect
	u in focus
ch	chin, arch
ng	ring, singer
sh	she, dash
th	thin, truth
th	then, father
zh	s in pleasure
´	as in (ā´b'l)

blood·hound (blud′hound) *n.* a large dog with a wrinkled face and long, drooping ears. Bloodhounds have a keen sense of smell and are often used in tracking escaped prisoners.

blouse (blous) *n.* a loose outer garment like a shirt, worn by women and children.

blue·ber·ry (bloo′ber′ē) *n.* ☆1 a small, round, dark blue berry that is eaten. ☆2 the shrub on which it grows. —*pl.* **blue′ber′ries**

bod·y (bäd′ē) *n.* the whole physical part of a person or animal [Athletes have strong *bodies.*]

Bos·ton (bôs′t′n) a seaport that is the capital of Massachusetts.

bot·tom (bät′əm) *n.* the lowest part [Sign your name at the *bottom* of this paper.] ◆*adj.* of or at the bottom; lowest [the *bottom* shelf].

bought (bôt) *past tense and past participle of* **buy.**

brake (brāk) *n.* a device used to slow down or stop a car, machine, etc. It is often a block or band that is pressed against a wheel or other moving part. ◆*v.* to slow down or stop with a brake. —**braked, brak′ing**

branch (branch) *n.* any part of a tree growing from the trunk or from a main limb. ◆*v.* to divide into branches [The road *branches* two miles east of town.]

break (brāk) *v.* 1 to come or make come apart by force; split or crack sharply into pieces [*Break* an egg into the bowl. The rusty hinge *broke.*] 2 to do better than; outdo [He *broke* the record for running the mile.] ◆*n.* 1 a broken place [The X ray showed a *break* in the bone.] 2 an interruption [Recess is a relaxing *break* in our school day.]

brick·lay·er (brik′lā′ər) *n.* a person whose work is building with bricks. —**brick′lay′ing** *n.*

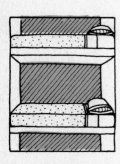

bunk

bright (brīt) *adj.* 1 shining; giving light; full of light [a *bright* star; a *bright* day]. 2 having a quick mind; clever [a *bright* child]. —**bright′ly** *adv.* —**bright′ness** *n.*

bring (bring) *v.* to carry or lead here or to the place where the speaker will be [*Bring* it to my house tomorrow.] —**brought, bring′ing**

bro·ken (brō′kən) *past participle of* **break.** ◆*adj.* 1 split or cracked into pieces [a *broken* dish; a *broken* leg]. 2 not in working condition [a *broken* watch].

brook (brook) *n.* a small stream.

broom (broom) *n.* a brush with a long handle, used for sweeping.

brush (brush) *n.* a bunch of bristles, hairs, or wires fastened into a hard back or handle. Brushes are used for cleaning, polishing, grooming, painting, etc. ◆*v.* 1 to use a brush on; clean, polish, paint, smooth, etc., with a brush [*Brush* your shoes. *Brush* the paint on evenly.] 2 to touch or graze in passing [The tire of the car *brushed* against the curb.]

build·er (bil′dər) *n.* one that builds; especially, a person whose business is putting up houses and other buildings.

bump·er (bum′pər) *n.* ☆a bar across the front or back of a car or truck to give it protection if it bumps into something.

bunch (bunch) *n.* a group of things of the same kind growing or placed together [a *bunch* of bananas; a *bunch* of keys].

bunk (bungk) *n.* a bed that sticks out from the wall like a shelf. ◆*v.* ☆to sleep in a bunk.

bush (boosh) *n.* a woody plant, smaller than a tree and having many stems branching out low instead of one main stem or trunk; shrub.

buy (bī) **v.** to get by paying money or something else [The Dutch *bought* Manhattan Island for about $24.] —**bought, buy′ing** ◆**n.** the value of a thing compared with its price [Turnips are your best *buy* in January vegetables.]

Cc

cage (kāj) **n.** a box or closed-off space with wires or bars on the sides, in which to keep birds or animals. ◆**v.** to shut up in a cage. —**caged, cag′ing**

cal·en·dar (kal′ən dər) **n.** **1** a system for arranging time into days, weeks, months, and years [Most countries now use the Gregorian *calendar*.] **2** a table or chart showing such an arrangement, usually for a single year [an old 1970 *calendar*].

calf¹ (kaf) **n.** **1** a young cow or bull. **2** a young elephant, whale, hippopotamus, seal, etc. —*pl.* **calves**

calf² (kaf) **n.** the fleshy back part of the leg between the knee and the ankle. —*pl.* **calves**

camp (kamp) **n.** a place in the country where people, especially children, can have an outdoor vacation. ◆**v.** to live in a camp or in the outdoors for a time [We'll be *camping* in Michigan this summer.]

☆**camp·site** (kamp′sīt) **n.** any place for a camp or for camping.

can·dy (kan′dē) **n.** a sweet food made from sugar or syrup, with flavor, coloring, fruits, nuts, etc., added. —*pl.* **can′dies**

can·not (kan′ät *or* kə nät′) *the usual way of writing* can not.

care (ker) **n.** a watching over or tending; protection [The books were left in my *care*.] ◆**v.** **1** to watch over or take charge of something [Will you *care* for my canary while I'm gone?] **2** to feel a liking [I don't *care* for dancing.] —**cared, car′ing**

car·pen·ter (kär′pən tər) **n.** a worker who builds and repairs wooden things, especially the wooden parts of buildings, ships, etc.

car·ry (kar′ē) **v.** to take from one place to another; transport or conduct [Please help me *carry* these books home. The large pipe *carries* water. Air *carries* sounds.] —**car′ried, car′ry·ing**

case (kās) **n.** a container for holding and protecting something [a watch*case*; a seed*case*; a violin *case*].

cash (kash) **n.** **1** money that one actually has, in coins or bills. **2** money or a check paid at the time of buying something [I always pay *cash* and never charge things.] ◆**v.** to give or get cash for [to *cash* a check].

catch (kach) **v.** **1** to stop by grasping with the hands or arms [to *catch* a ball]. **2** to become sick or infected with [to *catch* the flu]. —**caught, catch′ing** ◆**n.** **1** the act of catching a ball, etc. [The outfielder made a running *catch*.] **2** anything that is caught [a *catch* of 14 fish].

cat·tle (kat′'l) **n.pl.** animals of the cow family that are raised on farms and ranches, as cows, bulls, steers, and oxen.

caught (kôt) *past tense and past participle of* **catch**.

chair (cher) **n.** a piece of furniture that has a back and is a seat for one person.

calf

a	ask, fat
ā	ape, date
ä	car, lot
e	elf, ten
er	berry, care
ē	even, meet
i	is, hit
ir	mirror, here
ī	ice, fire
ō	open, go
ô	law, horn
oi	oil, point
oo	look, pull
o͞o	ooze, tool
yoo	unite, cure
yo͞o	cute, few
ou	out, crowd
u	up, cut
ʉr	fur, fern
ə	a in ago
	e in agent
	e in father
	i in unity
	o in collect
	u in focus
ch	chin, arch
ŋ	ring, singer
sh	she, dash
th	thin, truth
th	then, father
zh	s in pleasure
′	as in (ā′b'l)

chart

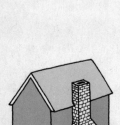

chimney

chalk (chôk) *n.* **1** a whitish limestone that is soft and easily crushed into a powder. It is made up mainly of tiny sea shells. **2** a piece of chalk or material like it, for writing on chalkboards.

change (chānj) *v.* **1** to make or become different in some way; alter [Time *changes* all things. His voice began to *change* at the age of thirteen.] **2** to put or take one thing in place of another; substitute [to *change* one's clothes; to *change* jobs]. —**changed, chang'ing** ◆ *n.* **1** the act of changing in some way [There will be a *change* in the weather tomorrow.] **2** something put in place of something else [a fresh *change* of clothing]. **3** the money returned when one has paid more than the amount owed [If it costs 70 cents and you pay with a dollar, you get back 30 cents as *change.*]

chap·ter (chap'tər) *n.* any of the main parts into which a book is divided.

chart (chärt) *n.* **1** a map, especially one for use in steering a ship or guiding an aircraft [A sailor's *chart* shows coastlines, depths, currents, etc.] **2** a group of facts about something set up in the form of a diagram, graph, table, etc. ◆ *v.* to make a map of.

chase (chās) *v.* to go after or keep following in order to catch or harm [The fox was *chasing* a rabbit.] —**chased, chas'ing**

cheap (chēp) *adj.* low in price [Vegetables are *cheaper* in summer than in winter.] ◆ *adv.* at a low cost [I bought these shoes *cheap* at a sale.] —**cheap'ly** *adv.* —**cheap'ness** *n.*

check (chek) *n.* **1** the mark ✓, used to show that something is right or to call attention to something. **2** a written order to a bank to pay a certain amount of money from one's account to a certain person. ◆ *v.* ☆to prove to be right or find what is wanted

by examining, comparing, etc. [These figures *check* with mine. *Check* the records for this information.]

cheer (chir) *n.* **1** a glad, excited shout of welcome, joy, or approval [The crowd gave the team three *cheers.*] **2** good or glad feelings; joy, hope, etc. [a visit that brought *cheer* to the invalid]. ◆ *v.* **1** to make or become glad or hopeful [Things are getting better, so *cheer* up!] **2** to urge on or applaud with cheers.

cher·ry (cher'ē) *n.* a small, round fruit with sweet flesh covering a smooth, hard seed. Cherries are bright red, dark red, or yellow. —*pl.* **cher'ries**

chew (chōō) *v.* to bite and grind up with the teeth.

chew·y (chōō'ē) *adj.* needing much chewing [*chewy* candy]. —**chew'i·er, chew'i·est**

child (chīld) *n.* **1** a baby; infant. **2** a young boy or girl. **3** a son or daughter [Their *children* are all grown up.] —*pl.* **chil'dren**

chil·dren (chil'drən) *n.* *plural of* **child**.

chil·ly (chil'ē) *adj.* so cool as to be uncomfortable; rather cold [a *chilly* room]. —**chil'li·er, chil'li·est**

chim·ney (chim'nē) *n.* a pipe or shaft going up through a roof to carry off smoke from a furnace, fireplace, or stove. Chimneys are usually enclosed with brick or stone. —*pl.* **chim'neys**

choice (chois) *n.* **1** the act of choosing or picking; selection [You may have a dessert of your own *choice.*] **2** a person or thing chosen [Green is my *choice* for mayor.] —**choic'er, choic'est**

choose (chōōz) *v.* to pick out one or more from a number or group [*Choose* a subject from this list.] —**chose, cho'sen, choos'ing**

cir·cus (sur′kəs) *n.* a traveling show held in tents or in a hall, with clowns, trained animals, acrobats, etc.

class (klas) *n.* ☆a group of students meeting together to be taught; also, a meeting of this kind [My English *class* is held at 9 o'clock.]

clean (klēn) *adj.* **1** without dirt or impure matter [*clean* dishes; *clean* oil]. **2** neat and tidy [to keep a *clean* desk]. ◆*v.* to make clean. [Please *clean* the oven.]

clear (klir) *adj.* **1** bright or sunny; without clouds or mist [a *clear* day]. **2** that can be seen through; transparent [*clear* glass]. **3** without anything in the way; not blocked; open [a *clear* view; a *clear* passage]. ◆*adv.* in a clear manner; clearly [The bells rang out *clear*.] ◆*v.* to empty or remove [*Clear* the snow from the sidewalk. Help me *clear* the table of dishes.] —**clear′ly** *adv.* —**clear′ness** *n.*

climb (klīm) *v.* to go up, or sometimes down, by using the feet and often the hands [to *climb* the stairs; to *climb* up or down a tree]. ◆*n.* the act of climbing; rise; ascent [a tiring *climb*]. —**climb′er** *n.*

close (klōs) *adj.* **1** with not much space between; near [The old houses are too *close* to each other.] **2** thorough or careful [Pay *close* attention.] —**clos′er, clos′est** ◆*adv.* so as to be close or near; closely [Follow *close* behind the leader.] —**close′ly** *adv.* —**close′ness** *n.*

clown (kloun) *n.* **1** a person who entertains, as in a circus, by doing comical tricks and silly stunts; jester; buffoon. **2** a person who likes to make jokes or act in a comical way [the *clown* of our family].

clue (kloō) *n.* a fact or thing that helps to solve a puzzle or mystery [Muddy footprints were a *clue* to the man's guilt.]

cock·er spaniel (käk′ər) a small dog with long, drooping ears, long, silky hair, and short legs.

coin (koin) *n.* a piece of metal money having a certain value.

col·lar (käl′ər) *n.* **1** the part of a garment that fits around the neck. It is sometimes a separate piece or a band that is folded over. **2** the part of a horse's harness that fits around its neck.

Col·o·rad·o (käl′ə rad′ō *or* käl′ə rä′dō) **1** a state in the southwestern part of the U.S.: abbreviated **Colo., CO 2** a river flowing southwest through Colorado.

☆**Co·lum·bi·a** (kə lum′bē ə) **1** the capital of South Carolina. **2** a river rising in British Columbia and flowing between Washington and Oregon to the Pacific.

com·ma (käm′ə) *n.* a punctuation mark (,) used to show a pause that is shorter than the pause at the end of a sentence [The *comma* is often used between clauses or after the opening phrase of a sentence. Words, numbers, or phrases in a series are separated by *commas*.]

com·pare (kəm per′) *v.* **1** to describe as being the same; liken [The sound of thunder can be *compared* to the roll of drums.] **2** to examine certain things in order to find out how they are alike or different [How do the two cars *compare* in size and price?] —**com·pared′, com·par′ing**

cone (kōn) *n.* **1** a solid object that narrows evenly from a flat circle at one end to a point at the other. **2** anything shaped like this, as a shell of pastry for holding ice cream. **3** the fruit of some evergreen trees, containing the seeds.

con·tain (kən tān′) *v.* to have in it; hold; enclose or include [This bottle *contains* cream. Your list *contains* 25 names.]

a	ask, fat
ā	ape, date
ä	car, lot
e	elf, ten
er	berry, care
ē	even, meet
i	is, hit
ir	mirror, here
ī	ice, fire
ō	open, go
ô	law, horn
oi	oil, point
oo	look, pull
ōō	ooze, tool
yoo	unite, cure
yōō	cute, few
ou	out, crowd
u	up, cut
ur	fur, fern
ə	a in ago
	e in agent
	e in father
	i in unity
	o in collect
	u in focus
ch	chin, arch
ng	ring, singer
sh	she, dash
th	thin, truth
th	then, father
zh	s in pleasure
′	as in (ā′b'l)

157

cooler

crown

cook·ie or **cook·y** (kook′ē) *n.* ☆a small, flat, sweet cake. —*pl.* **cook′ies**

cool·er (kool′ər) *n.* a container or room in which things are cooled or kept cool.

cop·y (käp′ē) *n.* **1** a thing made just like another; imitation or likeness [four carbon *copies* of a letter]. **2** any one of a number of books, magazines, pictures, etc., with the same printed matter [a library with six *copies* of *Tom Sawyer*]. —*pl.* **cop′ies** ◆*v.* **1** to make a copy or copies of [*Copy* the questions that are on the chalkboard.] **2** to act or be the same as; imitate. —**cop′ied, cop′y·ing**

cord (kôrd) *n.* **1** a thick string or thin rope. **2** any part of the body that is like a cord [the spinal *cord*; vocal *cords*]. **3** a wire or wires covered with rubber or other insulation and used to carry electricity from an outlet to a lamp, appliance, etc.

cor·ne·a (kôr′nē ə) *n.* the clear outer layer of the eyeball, covering the iris and the pupil.

cost (kôst) *v.* to be priced at; be sold for [It *costs* a dime.] —**cost, cost′ing** ◆*n.* amount of money, time, work, etc., asked or paid for something; price [the high *cost* of meat].

cot (kät) *n.* a narrow bed, as one made of canvas on a frame that can be folded up.

cough (kôf) *v.* **1** to force air from the lungs with a sudden, loud noise, as to clear the throat. **2** to get out of the throat by coughing [to *cough* up phlegm]. ◆*n.* a condition of coughing often [I have a bad *cough*.]

could·n't (kood′′nt) could not.

cou·pon (koo′pän *or* kyoo′pän) *n.* **1** a ticket or part of a ticket that gives the holder certain rights [The *coupon* on the cereal box is worth 10¢ toward buying another box.] **2** a part of a printed advertisement that can be used for ordering goods, samples, etc.

crawl (krôl) *v.* to move slowly by dragging the body along the ground as a worm does. ◆*n.* a crawling; slow, creeping movement.

cra·zy (krā′zē) *adj.* **1** mentally ill; insane. **2** very foolish or mad [a *crazy* idea]. —**cra′zi·er, cra′zi·est** —**cra′zi·ly** *adv.* —**cra′zi·ness** *n.*

creek (krēk *or* krik) *n.* a small stream, a little larger than a brook.

crib (krib) *n.* a small bed with high sides, for a baby.

crowd (kroud) *n.* a large group of people together [*crowds* of Christmas shoppers]. ◆*v.* to push or squeeze [Can we all *crowd* into one car?]

crown (kroun) *n.* a headdress of gold, jewels, etc., worn by a king or queen. ◆*v.* to make a king or queen by putting a crown on [Elizabeth I was *crowned* in 1558.]

cut (kut) *v.* **1** to make an opening in with a knife or other sharp tool; pierce; gash [Andy *cut* his chin while shaving.] **2** to divide into parts with such a tool; sever [Will you *cut* the cake?] **3** to make shorter by trimming [to *cut* one's hair]. **4** to go through or across, usually to make a shorter way [The path *cuts* across the meadow. The tunnel *cuts* through the mountain.] —**cut, cut′ting**

Dal·las (dal′əs) a city in northeastern Texas.

Dal·ma·tian (dal mā′shən) *n.* a large dog with short hair and a black-and-white coat.

dance (dans) *v.* to move the body and feet in some kind of rhythm, usually to music [to *dance* a waltz or a minuet].
—**danced, danc'ing**

dan·ger (dān'jər) *n.* **1** a condition in which there could be harm, trouble, loss, etc.; risk; peril [to live in constant *danger*]. **2** something that may cause harm [Jungle explorers face many *dangers*.]

dash (dash) *v.* to move quickly; rush [The thief *dashed* down the alley.] ◆*n.* **1** a little bit; pinch [Put a *dash* of salt in the salad.] ☆**2** a short, fast run or race [a 100-yard *dash*]. **3** the mark (—), used in printing or writing to show a break in a sentence or to show that something has been left out.

dead (ded) *adj.* no longer living; without life [Throw out those *dead* flowers.] ◆*adv.* completely; entirely [I am *dead* tired from running.] ◆*n.* the time of most cold, most darkness, etc. [the *dead* of winter; the *dead* of night].

De·cem·ber (di sem'bər) *n.* the last month of the year, which has 31 days: abbreviated **Dec.**

deer (dir) *n.* a swift-running, hoofed animal that chews its cud. The male usually has antlers that are shed every year. —*pl.* **deer**

Den·ver (den'vər) the capital of Colorado.

desk (desk) *n.* a piece of furniture with a smooth top at which one can write, draw, or read. It often has drawers for storing things.

di·al (dī'əl) *n.* **1** the face of a watch, clock, or sundial. ☆**2** a disk on a telephone that can be turned for making connections automatically. ◆*v.* **1** to tune in a radio or TV station. ☆**2** to call on a telephone by using a dial.
—**di'aled** or **di'alled, di'al·ing** or **di'al·ling**

did·n't (did''nt) did not.

dif·fer·ence (dif'ər əns *or* dif'rəns) *n.* **1** the state of being different or unlike [the *difference* between right and wrong]. **2** a way in which people or things are unlike [a *difference* in size]. **3** the amount by which one quantity is greater or less than another [The *difference* between 11 and 7 is 4.]

dig (dig) *v.* **1** to turn up or remove ground with a spade, the hands, claws, etc. [The children are *digging* in the sand.] **2** to make by digging [to *dig* a well].
—**dug** or *in older use* **digged, dig'ging**

dis·ap·pear (dis ə pir') *v.* to stop being seen or to stop existing; vanish [The car *disappeared* around a curve. Dinosaurs *disappeared* millions of years ago.] —**dis'ap·pear'ance** *n.*

dis·cov·er (dis kuv'ər) *v.* to be the first to find, see, or learn about [Marie and Pierre Curie *discovered* radium.]

dish (dish) *n.* any of the plates, bowls, saucers, etc., used to serve food at the table. ◆*v.* to serve in a dish [*Dish* up the beans.]
—**dish'ful** *adj.*

dis·like (dis līk') *v.* to have a feeling of not liking; be opposed to [I *dislike* people I can't trust.]
—**dis·liked', dis·lik'ing** ◆*n.* a feeling of not liking; distaste [The gardener felt a strong *dislike* for toads.]

dis·o·bey (dis ə bā') *v.* to fail to obey or refuse to obey.

dis·or·der (dis ôr'dər) *n.* lack of order; jumble; confusion [The troops retreated in *disorder*.]

dis·please (dis plēz') *v.* to make angry or not satisfied; annoy.
—**dis·pleased', dis·pleas'ing**

dis·trust (dis trust') *n.* a lack of trust; doubt; suspicion. ◆*v.* to have no trust in; doubt.
—**dis·trust'ful** *adj.*

desk

a	ask, fat
ā	ape, date
ä	car, lot
e	elf, ten
er	berry, care
ē	even, meet
i	is, hit
ir	mirror, here
ī	ice, fire
ō	open, go
ô	law, horn
oi	oil, point
oo	look, pull
ōō	ooze, tool
yoo	unite, cure
yōō	cute, few
ou	out, crowd
u	up, cut
ʉr	fur, fern
ə	**a** in ago
	e in agent
	e in father
	i in unity
	o in collect
	u in focus
ch	chin, arch
ng	ring, singer
sh	she, dash
th	thin, truth
th	then, father
zh	s in pleasure
'	as in (ā'b'l)

ditch (dich) *n.* a long, narrow opening dug in the earth, as for carrying off water; trench [a *ditch* along the road].

do (doo͞) *v.* **1** to work at or carry out an action; perform [What do you *do* for a living? I'll *do* the job.] **2** to bring about; cause [The storm *did* a lot of damage.] **3** to put forth; exert [She *did* her best.] **4** to take care of; attend to [Who will *do* the dishes?] —**did, done, do′ing**

does (duz) *the form of the verb* **do** *showing the present time with singular nouns and with* he, she, *or* it.

does·n't (duz′'nt) does not.

don't (dōnt) do not.

dress·ing (dres′ing) *n.* **1** a bandage or medicine for a wound or sore. **2** a sauce, as of oil, vinegar, and seasoning, added to salads and other dishes. **3** a stuffing, as of bread and seasoning, for roast chicken, turkey, etc.

drift (drift) *v.* **1** to be carried along by a current of water or air [The raft *drifted* downstream. The leaves *drifted* to the ground.] **2** to pile up in heaps by the force of wind [The snow *drifted* against the door.] ◆*n.* a pile formed by the force of wind or water [a *drift* of sand along the shore].

drive (drīv) *v.* to control the movement of an automobile, horse and wagon, bus, etc. —**drove, driv′en, driv′ing** ◆*n.* **1** a trip in an automobile, etc. **2** a street, road, or driveway.

drone (drōn) *n.* a male honeybee. It has no sting and does no work. ◆*v.* to make a humming or buzzing sound [The planes *droned* overhead.] —**droned, dron′ing**

drove (drōv) *past tense of* **drive**.

dry (drī) *adj.* **1** not wet or damp; without moisture. **2** having little or no rain or water [a *dry* summer]. **3** thirsty. —**dri′er, dri′est** ◆*v.* to make or become

dry. —**dried, dry′ing** —**dry′ly** *adv.* —**dry′ness** *n.*

dug (dug) *past tense and past participle of* **dig**.

Ee

each (ēch) *adj., pron.* every one of two or more, thought of separately [*Each* pupil will receive a book. *Each* of the books is numbered.] ◆*adv.* for each; apiece [The tickets cost $5.00 *each*.]

ea·ger (ē′gər) *adj.* wanting very much; anxious to do or get [*eager* to win; *eager* for praise]. —**ea′ger·ly** *adv.* —**ea′ger·ness** *n.*

ear·ly (ur′lē) *adv., adj.* **1** near the beginning; soon after the start [in the *early* afternoon; *early* in his career]. **2** before the usual or expected time [The bus arrived *early*.] —**ear′li·er, ear′li·est** —**ear′li·ness** *n.*

earth (urth) *n.* **1** the planet that we live on. It is the fifth largest planet and the third in distance away from the sun. **2** the dry part of the earth's surface, that is not the sea. **3** soil or ground [a flowerpot filled with good, rich *earth*].

east (ēst) *n.* **1** the direction toward the point where the sun rises. **2** a place or region in or toward this direction. ◆*adj.* in, of, to, or toward the east [the *east* bank of the river]. ◆*adv.* in or toward the east [Go *east* ten miles.]

egg (eg) *n.* the oval or round body that is laid by a female bird, fish, reptile, insect, etc., and from which a young bird, fish, etc., is later hatched. It has a brittle shell or tough outer skin.

eight (āt) *n., adj.* one more than seven; the number 8.

eighth (ātth) *adj.* coming after seven others; 8th in order. ◆*n.* one of eight equal parts of something; 1/8.

ditch

drone

el·e·phant (el′ə fənt) *n.* a huge animal with a thick skin, two ivory tusks, and a long snout, or trunk. It is found in Africa and India and is the largest of the four-legged animals.

e·lev·enth (i lev′ənth) *adj.* coming after ten others; 11th in order. ◆*n.* one of the eleven equal parts of something; 1/11.

else (els) *adj.* **1** not the same; different; other [I thought you were someone *else*.] **2** that may be added; more [Do you want anything *else*?] ◆*adv.* in a different time, place, or way [Where *else* did you go?]

emp·ty (emp′tē) *adj.* having nothing or no one in it; not occupied; vacant [an *empty* jar; an *empty* house]. —**emp′ti·er, emp′ti·est** ◆*v.* to take out or pour out [*Empty* the dirty water in the sink.] —**emp′tied, emp′ty·ing** —*pl.* **emp′ties** —**emp′ti·ly** *adv.* —**emp′ti·ness** *n.*

en·gine (en′jən) *n.* **1** a machine that uses energy of some kind to create motion and do work [An automobile *engine* uses the energy of hot gases formed by exploding gasoline.] **2** a railroad locomotive.

en·joy (in joi′) *v.* to get joy or pleasure from [We *enjoyed* the baseball game.]

ev·er·y (ev′rē) *adj.* **1** all the group of which the thing named is one; each [*Every* student must take the test. She has read *every* book on the list.] **2** all that there could be [You've been given *every* chance.]

ev·er·y·where (ev′rē hwer) *adv.* in or to every place [*Everywhere* I go I meet friends.]

eye (ī) *n.* the part of the body with which a human being or animal sees. ◆*v.* to look at; observe [We *eyed* the stranger suspiciously.] —**eyed, ey′ing**

face (fās) *n.* the front part of the head, including the eyes, nose, and mouth. ◆*v.* to turn toward or have the face turned toward [Please *face* the class. Our house *faces* a park.] —**faced, fac′ing**

fail (fāl) *v.* **1** to not do what one tried to do or what one should have done; not succeed; miss or neglect [She *failed* as a singer. He *failed* to keep his promise.] **2** to give or get a grade that shows one has not passed a test, a school course, etc.

fam·i·ly (fam′ə lē) *n.* **1** a group made up of two parents and all of their children. **2** a group of people who are related by marriage or a common ancestor; relatives; clan. —*pl.* **fam′i·lies**

farm·er (fär′mər) *n.* a person who owns or works on a farm.

fast¹ (fast) *adj.* moving, working, etc., at high speed; rapid; quick; swift [a *fast* pace; a *fast* reader]. ◆*adv.* **1** at a high speed; swiftly; rapidly [arrested for driving too *fast*]. **2** in a complete way; soundly; thoroughly [*fast* asleep].

fast² (fast) *v.* to go without any food or certain foods, as in following the rules of one's religion.

feast (fēst) *n.* a large meal with many courses; banquet. ◆*v.* to eat a big or rich meal.

feel (fēl) *v.* **1** to touch in order to find out something [*Feel* the baby's bottle to see if the milk is warm.] **2** to be aware of through the senses or the mind [He *felt* rain on his face. Do you *feel* pain in this tooth?] **3** to think or believe [She *feels* that we should go.] —**felt, feel′ing** ◆*n.* the way a thing feels to the touch [It seems to be all wool by the *feel* of it.]

elephant

a	ask, fat
ā	ape, date
ä	car, lot
e	elf, ten
er	berry, care
ē	even, meet
i	is, hit
ir	mirror, here
ī	ice, fire
ō	open, go
ô	law, horn
oi	oil, point
oo	look, pull
o͞o	ooze, tool
yoo	unite, cure
yo͞o	cute, few
ou	out, crowd
u	up, cut
ur	fur, fern
ə	a in ago
	e in agent
	e in father
	i in unity
	o in collect
	u in focus
ch	chin, arch
ng	ring, singer
sh	she, dash
th	thin, truth
th	then, father
zh	s in pleasure
′	as in (ā′b'l)

felt[1] (felt) **n.** a heavy material made of wool, fur, or hair pressed together under heat. ◆**adj.** made of felt [a *felt* hat].

felt[2] (felt) *past tense and past participle of* **feel**.

fifth (fifth) **adj.** coming after four others; 5th in order. ◆**n.** one of five equal parts of something; 1/5.

fight (f ī t) **v.** to use fists, weapons, or other force in trying to beat or overcome someone or something; battle; struggle [to *fight* hand to hand; to *fight* a war]. —**fought, fight′ing** ◆**n.** the use of force to beat or overcome someone or something; battle.

fin·ish (fin′ish) **v.** to bring or come to an end; complete or become completed [Did you *finish* your work?   The game *finished* early.] ◆**n.** **1** the last part; end [The audience stayed to the *finish*.] **2** the kind of surface a thing has [an oil *finish* on wood]. —**fin′ished adj.**

first (furst) **adj.** before another or before all others in time, order, quality, etc.; earliest, foremost, etc. [the *first* snow of winter; the *first* door to the right; *first* prize]. ◆**adv.** before anything or anyone else [*First* we had soup.   Guests are served *first*.] ◆**n.** **1** the one that is first [to be the *first* to succeed]. **2** the beginning; start [At *first*, I believed him.]

fish (fish) **n.** an animal that lives in water and has a backbone, fins, and gills for breathing. Most fish are covered with scales. —*pl.* **fish** (or when different kinds are meant, **fishes**) [She caught three *fish*.   The aquarium exhibits many *fishes*.] ◆**v.** to catch or try to catch fish.

flash·light (flash′līt) **n.** an electric light that uses batteries and is small enough to carry.

flashlight

flaw (flô) **n.** a break, scratch, crack, etc., that spoils something; blemish [There is a *flaw* in this diamond.] —**flaw′less adj.** —**flaw′less·ly adv.**

flex (fleks) **v.** **1** to bend [to *flex* an arm]. **2** to make tighter and harder; contract [to *flex* a muscle].

float (flōt) **v.** **1** to rest on top of water or other liquid and not sink [Ice *floats*.] **2** to move or drift slowly, as on a liquid or through the air [Clouds *floated* overhead.] ◆**n.** a platform on wheels that carries a display or exhibit in a parade. —**float′er n.**

floor (flôr) **n.** the bottom part of a room, hall, etc., on which to walk.

flow·er (flou′ər) **n.** the part of a plant that bears the seed and usually has brightly colored petals; blossom or bloom. ◆**v.** to come into bloom; bear flowers.

fly[1] (flī) **v.** **1** to move through the air by using wings, as a bird. **2** to travel or carry through the air, as in an aircraft. —**flew, flown, fly′ing**

fly[2] (flī) **n.** **1** a flying insect having one pair of wings, as the housefly and gnat. —*pl.* **flies**

fog (fôg *or* fäg) **n.** **1** a large mass of tiny drops of water, near the earth's surface; thick mist that makes it hard to see. **2** a condition of being confused or bewildered. —**fogged, fog′ging**

fog·gy (fôg′ē *or* fäg′ē) **adj.** **1** having fog [a *foggy* day]. **2** mixed up; confused [a *foggy* idea]. —**fog′gi·er, fog′gi·est** —**fog′gi·ly adv.** —**fog′gi·ness n.**

foil[1] (foil) **v.** to keep from doing something; thwart; stop [Their evil plans were *foiled* again.]

foil[2] (foil) **n.** a very thin sheet of metal [aluminum *foil*].

for·est (fôr′ist) **n.** many trees growing closely together over a large piece of land; large woods. ◆**v.** to plant with trees.

fork (fôrk) *n.* **1** a tool with a handle at one end and two or more points or prongs at the other, used to pick up something. Small forks are used in eating, and large forks, as pitchforks, are used for tossing hay and manure on a farm. ☆**2** the point where something divides into two or more branches [the *fork* of a road or of a tree]. ◆*v.* to divide into branches [Go left where the road *forks*.]

fought (fôt) *past tense and past participle of* **fight.**

four (fôr) *n., adj.* one more than three; the number 4.

fourth (fôrth) *adj.* coming after three others; 4th in order. ◆*n.* one of four equal parts of something; 1/4.

frame (frām) *n.* **1** the support or skeleton around which a thing is built and that gives the thing its shape; framework [the *frame* of a house]. **2** the border or case into which a window, door, picture, etc., is set. ◆*v.* **1** to put a frame, or border, around [to *frame* a picture]. ☆**2** to make an innocent person seem guilty by a plot: *used only in everyday talk.* —**framed, fram′ing**

free (frē) *adj.* **1** not under the control of another; not a slave or not in prison. **2** able to vote and to speak, write, meet, and worship as one pleases; having political and civil liberty. **3** not tied up, fastened, or shut in; loose [As soon as the bird was *free*, it flew away.] **4** with no charge; without cost [*free* tickets to the ball game]. —**fre′er, fre′est** ◆*v.* to make free [The governor *freed* five prisoners by granting pardons.] —**freed, free′ing.**

fresh (fresh) *adj.* **1** newly made, got, or grown; not spoiled, stale, etc. [*fresh* coffee; *fresh* eggs]. **2** cool and clean [*fresh* air]. —**fresh′ly** *adv.* —**fresh′ness** *n.*

Fri·day (frī′dē *or* frī′dā) *n.* the sixth day of the week.

friend (frend) *n.* a person whom one knows well and likes.

fright (frīt) *n.* **1** sudden fear; alarm. **2** something that looks so strange or ugly as to startle one [That old fur coat is a perfect *fright*.]

frown (froun) *v.* to wrinkle the forehead and draw the eyebrows together in anger, worry, or deep thought. ◆*n.* a frowning or the look one has in frowning.

fro·zen (frōz′'n) *past participle of* **freeze.** ◆*adj.* turned into or covered with ice [a *frozen* pond].

fu·el (fyōō′'l) *n.* anything that is burned to give heat or power [Coal, gas, oil, and wood are *fuels*.] ◆*v.* to supply with fuel. —**fu′eled** or **fu′elled, fu′el·ing** or **fu′el·ling**

fume (fyōōm) *n.* *often* **fumes**, *pl.* a gas, smoke, or vapor, especially if harmful or bad-smelling. ◆*v.* **1** to give off fumes. **2** to show that one is angry or irritated [He *fumed* at the long delay.] —**fumed, fum′ing**

frame

Gg

gar·den (gär′d'n) *n.* a piece of ground where flowers, vegetables, etc., are grown. ◆*v.* to take care of a garden. —**gar·den·er** (gärd′nər) *n.*

geese (gēs) *n.* *plural of* **goose.**

gi·ant (jī′ənt) *n.* **1** an imaginary being that looks like a person but is many times larger and stronger. **2** a person or thing that is especially large, strong, etc. [Einstein was a mental *giant*.]

a	ask, fat
ā	ape, date
ä	car, lot
e	elf, ten
er	berry, care
ē	even, meet
i	is, hit
ir	mirror, here
ī	ice, fire
ō	open, go
ô	law, horn
oi	oil, point
ōō	look, pull
ōō	ooze, tool
yōō	unite, cure
yōō	cute, few
ou	out, crowd
u	up, cut
ur	fur, fern
ə	a in ago
	e in agent
	e in father
	i in unity
	o in collect
	u in focus
ch	chin, arch
ng	ring, singer
sh	she, dash
th	thin, truth
th	then, father
zh	s in pleasure
'	as in (ā′b'l)

163

give (giv) **v.** **1** to pass or hand over to another [*Give* me your coat and I'll hang it up.] **2** to hand over to another to keep; make a gift of [My uncle *gave* a book to me for my birthday.] —**gave, giv′en, giv′ing** —**giv′er n.**

glue (gloo) **n.** **1** a thick, sticky substance made by boiling animal hoofs and bones, used for sticking things together. **2** any sticky substance like this. ◆**v.** to stick together with glue. —**glued, glu′ing** —**glue′y adj.**

gob·ble¹ (gäb′'l) **n.** the throaty sound made by a male turkey. ◆**v.** to make this sound. —**gob′bled, gob′bling**

gob·ble² (gäb′'l) **v.** to eat quickly and greedily. —**gob′bled, gob′bling**

gone (gôn) *past participle of* **go.** ◆**adj.** **1** moved away; departed. **2** used up.

good·bye or **good-bye** (good bī′) **interj., n.** a word said when leaving someone; farewell [We said our *goodbyes* quickly and left.] —*pl.* **good·byes′** or **good-byes′**

good·ness (good′nis) **n.** the condition of being good. ◆**interj.** an exclamation showing surprise [My *goodness*! *Goodness* me!]

goose (goos) **n.** a swimming bird that is like a duck but has a larger body and a longer neck; especially, the female of this bird.— *pl.* **geese**

grape (grāp) **n.** **1** a small fruit with a smooth skin, usually purple, red, or green, that grows in bunches on a woody vine. Grapes are eaten raw and are used to make wine and raisins. **2** a grapevine.

graph (graf) **n.** a chart or diagram that shows the changes taking place in something, by the use of connected lines, a curve, etc. [a *graph* showing how sales figures vary during the year].

Monthly Sales
(in thousands of dollars)

graph

Great Dane

grate¹ (grāt) **v.** to grind into small bits or shreds by rubbing against a rough surface [to *grate* cabbage]. —**grat′ed, grat′ing**

grate² (grāt) **n.** **1** a frame of metal bars for holding fuel, as in a fireplace or furnace. **2** a framework of bars set in a window or door; grating.

great (grāt) **adj.** **1** much above the average in size, degree, power, etc.; big or very big; much or very much [the *Great* Lakes; a *great* distance; *great* pain]. **2** very important; noted; remarkable [a *great* composer; a *great* discovery]. **3** older or younger by a generation: *used in words formed with a hyphen* [my *great*-aunt; my *great*-niece]. —**great′ly adv.** —**great′ness n.**

Great Dane a very large dog with short, smooth hair.

grind (grīnd) **v.** **1** to crush into tiny bits or into powder [The miller *grinds* grain between millstones.] **2** to sharpen or smooth by rubbing against a rough surface [to *grind* a knife]. **3** to press down or rub together harshly or with a grating sound [She *ground* her teeth in anger.] —**ground, grind′ing**

ground¹ (ground) **n.** the solid part of the earth's surface; land; earth. ◆**adj.** of, on, or near the ground [the *ground* floor of a building].

ground² (ground) *past tense and past participle of* **grind.**

group (groop) **n.** a number of persons or things gathered together. ◆**v.** to gather together into a group [*Group* yourselves in a circle.]

gym (jim) **n.** **1** *a shorter form of* **gymnasium.** ☆**2** *another name for* **physical education.** *This word is used only in everyday talk.*

Hh

half (haf) *n.* either of the two equal parts of something [Five is *half* of ten.] —*pl.* **halves** ◆*adj.* being either of the two equal parts [a *half* gallon].

☆**hall·way** (hôl′wā) *n.* a passageway, as between rooms; corridor.

ham·mock (ham′ək) *n.* a long piece of canvas that is hung from ropes at each end and is used as a bed or couch.

haul (hôl) *v.* **1** to move by pulling; drag or tug [We *hauled* the boat up on the beach.] **2** to carry by wagon, truck, etc. [He *hauls* steel for a large company.] ◆*n.* the distance that something is hauled [It's a long *haul* to town.]

have·n't (hav′′nt) have not.

health (helth) *n.* the condition of being well in body and mind; freedom from sickness.

hear (hir) *v.* **1** to receive sound through the ears [I *hear* music. Pat doesn't *hear* well.] **2** to listen to; pay attention [*Hear* what I tell you.] —**heard** (hʉrd), **hear′ing**

heav·y (hev′ē) *adj.* hard to lift or move because of its weight; weighing very much [a *heavy* load]. —**heav′i·er, heav′i·est** —**heav′i·ly** *adv.* —**heav′i·ness** *n.*

hel·lo (he lō′ *or* hə lō′) *interj.* a word used in greeting someone or in answering the telephone. ◆*n.* a saying or calling of "hello." —*pl.* **hel·los′** ◆*v.* to say or call "hello." —**hel·loed′, hel·lo′ing**

help (help) *v.* **1** to give or do something that is needed or useful; make things easier for; aid; assist [We *helped* our poor relatives. *Help* me lift this.] **2** to make better; give relief to; remedy [This medicine will *help* your cold.] ◆*n.* the act of helping or a thing that helps; aid; assistance [Your advice was a great *help*.] —**help′er** *n.*

here (hir) *adv.* at or in this place [Who lives *here*?] ◆*interj.* a word called out to get attention, answer a roll call, etc. ◆*n.* this place [Let's get out of *here*.]

he·ro (hir′ō) *n.* **1** a person, especially a man or boy, who is looked up to for having done something brave or noble [He became a *hero* when he saved his family from a burning house. Washington was the *hero* of the American Revolution.] **2** the most important man in a novel, play, etc., especially if he is good or noble. —*pl.* **he′roes**

her·self (hər self′) *pron.* **1** her own self. *This form of* **she** *is used when the object is the same as the subject of the verb* [She cut *herself*.] **2** her usual or true self [She's not *herself* today.] *Herself is also used to give force to the subject* [She *herself* told me so.]

he's (hēz) **1** he is. **2** he has.

high·way (hī′wā) *n.* a main road.

him·self (him self′) *pron.* **1** his own self. *This form of* **he** *is used when the object is the same as the subject of the verb* [He hurt *himself*.] **2** his usual or true self [He isn't *himself* today.] *Himself is also used to give force to the subject* [He *himself* told us so.]

hive (hīv) *n.* **1** a box or other shelter for a colony of bees; beehive. **2** a colony of bees living in a hive. ◆*v.* to gather into a hive, as bees. —**hived, hiv′ing**

hon·ey (hun′ē) *n.* **1** a thick, sweet, yellow syrup that bees make from the nectar of flowers and store in honeycombs. **2** sweet one; darling: used in talking to someone dear to one [How are you, *honey*?]

hammock

hon·or (än′ər) *n.* **1** great respect given because of worth, noble deeds, high rank, etc. [to pay *honor* to the geniuses of science]. **2** something done or given as a sign of respect [Madame Curie received many *honors* for her work.] **3** good name or reputation [You must uphold the *honor* of the family.] **4** a being true to what is right, honest, etc. [Her sense of *honor* kept her from cheating.] ◆*v.* to have or show great respect for [America *honors* the memory of Lincoln. *Honor* your father and your mother.] ◆*adj.* of or showing honor [an *honor* roll].

hope (hōp) *n.* a feeling that what one wants will happen [We gave up *hope* of being rescued.] ◆*v.* **1** to have hope; want and expect [I *hope* to see you soon.] **2** to want to believe [I *hope* I didn't overlook anybody.] —**hoped, hop′ing**

ho·tel (hō tel′) *n.* a building where travelers may rent rooms, buy meals, etc.

hour (our) *n.* **1** any of the 24 equal parts of a day; 60 minutes. **2** a particular time [At what *hour* shall we meet?]

huge (hyo͞oj) *adj.* very large; immense [the *huge* trunk of the redwood tree]. —**huge′ly** *adv.* —**huge′ness** *n.*

hu·man (hyo͞o′mən) *adj.* that is a person or that has to do with people in general [a *human* being; *human* affairs]. ◆*n.* a person: *some people still prefer the full phrase* **human being.**

hun·gry (huŋ′grē) *adj.* **1** wanting or needing food [Cold weather makes me *hungry*.] **2** having a strong desire; eager [*hungry* for praise]. —**hun′gri·er, hun′gri·est** —**hun′gri·ly** *adv.* —**hun′gri·ness** *n.*

hunt·er (hun′tər) *n.* a person who hunts.

icicle

hur·ried (hur′ēd) *adj.* done or acting in a hurry; hasty [We ate a *hurried* lunch.] —**hur′ried·ly** *adv.*

hurt (hurt) *v.* **1** to cause pain or injury to; wound [The fall *hurt* my leg.] **2** to have pain [My head *hurts*.] **3** to harm or damage in some way [Water won't *hurt* this table top.] —**hurt, hurt′ing** ◆*n.* pain, injury, or harm [Warm water will ease the *hurt*.]

ice (īs) *n.* water frozen solid by cold [Water turns to *ice* at 0°C.] ◆*v.* **1** to change into ice; freeze [The lake *iced* over.] **2** to cover with icing, or frosting [to *ice* a cake]. —**iced, ic′ing**

i·ci·cle (ī′si k′l) *n.* a hanging stick of ice formed by water freezing as it drips down.

i·cy (ī′sē) *adj.* **1** full of or covered with ice [*icy* streets]. **2** like ice; slippery or very cold [*icy* fingers]. —**i′ci·er, i′ci·est** —**i′ci·ly** *adv.* —**i′ci·ness** *n.*

I'd (īd) **1** I had. **2** I would. **3** I should.

I'll (īl) **1** I shall. **2** I will.

inch (inch) *n.* a unit for measuring length, equal to 1/12 foot. One inch equals 2.54 centimeters. ◆*v.* to move a little at a time [Lou *inched* along the narrow ledge.]

inn (in) *n.* **1** a hotel that has a tavern or restaurant. **2** a tavern or restaurant.

in·side (in′sīd′) *n.* the side or part that is within; interior [Wash the windows on the *inside*.] ◆*adj.* on or in the inside; internal; indoor [*inside* work; an *inside* page].

in·to (in'tōō *or* in'tə) *prep.* **1** to the inside of [to go *into* the house]. **2** to the form, condition, etc., of [The farm has been turned *into* a park. They got *into* trouble.]

i·ris (ī'ris) *n.* **1** the colored part of the eye, around the pupil. *See the picture for* **eye.** **2** a plant with long leaves and showy flowers.

is·n't (iz''nt) is not.

it (it) *pron.* the animal or thing being talked about [I read that book and liked *it*.] ◆*n.* the player, as in the game of tag, who must try to touch, catch, or find another. —*pl.* **they**

itch (ich) *v.* to have a tickling feeling on the skin that makes one want to scratch; also, to cause to have this feeling [The wool shirt *itches* my skin.] ◆*n.* an itching feeling on the skin.

its (its) *pron.* of it or done by it: *the possessive form of* **it,** *thought of as an adjective* [Give the cat *its* dinner. The frost had done *its* damage.]

I've (īv) I have.

Jj

jack·et (jak'it) *n.* a short coat.

jeans (jēnz) *n.pl.* trousers or overalls made of a heavy, cotton cloth, usually blue.

jog (jäg) *v.* to move along slowly or steadily, but with a jolting motion. —**jogged, jog'ging** ◆*n.* a jogging pace; trot. —**jog'ger** *n.*

join (join) *v.* **1** to bring together; connect; fasten [We *joined* hands and stood in a circle.] **2** to become a part or member of [Paula has *joined* our club.] **3** to take part along with others [*Join* in the game.]

joke (jōk) *n.* anything said or done to get a laugh, as a funny story. ◆*v.* to tell or play jokes.

—**joked, jok'ing** —**jok'ing·ly** *adv.*

jug·gle (jug''l) *v.* to do skillful tricks with the hands; especially, to keep tossing a number of things up in the air one by one and keep them all moving. —**jug'gled, jug'gling** —**jug'gler** *n.*

Kk

keep (kēp) *v.* **1** to have or hold and not let go [He was *kept* after school. She kept her trim figure. Can you *keep* a secret?] **2** to hold for a later time; save [I *kept* the cake to eat later.] **3** to take care of; look after [He *keeps* house for himself.] **4** to stay or make stay as it is; last; continue [The fish will *keep* a while if you pack it in ice. *Keep* your engine running. *Keep* on walking.] —**kept, keep'ing**

kept (kept) *past tense and past participle of* **keep.**

kill (kil) *v.* **1** to cause the death of; make die; slay. **2** to put an end to; destroy or ruin [Her defeat *killed* all our hopes.] **3** to make time pass in doing unimportant things [an hour to *kill* before my train leaves]. ◆*n.* **1** the act of killing [to be in at the *kill*]. **2** an animal or animals killed [the lion's *kill*]. —**kill'er** *n.*

kind¹ (kīnd) *n.* sort or variety [all *kinds* of books].

kind² (kīnd) *adj.* **1** always ready to help others and do good; friendly, gentle, generous, sympathetic, etc. **2** showing goodness, generosity, sympathy, etc. [*kind* deeds; *kind* regards].

kitch·en (kich'ən) *n.* a room or place for preparing and cooking food.

knee (nē) *n.* the joint between the thigh and the lower leg.

knew (nōō *or* nyōō) *past tense of* **know.**

iris

a	ask, fat
ā	ape, date
ä	car, lot
e	elf, ten
er	berry, care
ē	even, meet
i	is, hit
ir	mirror, here
ī	ice, fire
ō	open, go
ô	law, horn
oi	oil, point
oo	look, pull
ōō	ooze, tool
yoo	unite, cure
yōō	cute, few
ou	out, crowd
u	up, cut
ur	fur, fern
ə	a in ago
	e in agent
	e in father
	i in unity
	o in collect
	u in focus
ch	chin, arch
ng	ring, singer
sh	she, dash
th	thin, truth
th	then, father
zh	s in pleasure
'	as in (ā'b'l)

167

knight

lantern

knife (nīf) *n.* a tool having a flat, sharp blade set in a handle, used for cutting. —*pl.* **knives** ◆ *v.* to cut or stab with a knife. —**knifed, knif′ing**

knight (nīt) *n.* a man in the Middle Ages who was given a military rank of honor after serving as a page and squire. Knights were supposed to be gallant and brave. ◆ *v.* to give the rank of knight to.

knives (nīvz) *n.* *plural of* **knife.**

knock (näk) *v.* **1** to hit as with the fist; especially, to rap on a door [Who is *knocking*?] **2** to hit and cause to fall [The dog *knocked* down the papergirl.] ◆ *n.* a hard, loud blow, as with the fist; rap, as on a door.

knot (nät) *n.* **1** a lump, as in a string or ribbon, formed by a loop or a tangle drawn tight. **2** a fastening made by tying together parts or pieces of string, rope, etc. [Sailors make a variety of *knots.*] ◆ *v.* **1** to tie or fasten with a knot; make a knot in. **2** to become tangled. —**knot′ted, knot′ting**

know (nō) *v.* **1** to be sure of or have the facts about [Do you *know* why grass is green? She *knows* the law.] **2** to have in one's mind or memory [The actress *knows* her lines.] **3** to be acquainted with [I *know* your brother well.] —**knew, known, know′ing**

Ll

la·dy (lā′dē) *n.* a woman, especially one who is polite and refined and has a sense of honor. —*pl.* **la′dies** ◆ *adj.* that is a woman; female [a *lady* barber].

lan·tern (lan′tərn) *n.* a case of glass, paper, etc., holding a light and protecting it from wind and rain.

large (lärj) *adj.* of great size or amount; big [a *large* house; a *large* sum of money]. —**larg′er, larg′est** ◆ *adv.* in a large way [Don't write so *large.*] —**large′ness** *n.*

late·ly (lāt′lē) *adv.* just before this time; not long ago; recently.

laugh (laf) *v.* to make a series of quick sounds with the voice that show one is amused or happy or, sometimes, that show scorn. One usually smiles or grins when laughing. ◆ *n.* the act or sound of laughing.

law (lô) *n.* all the rules that tell people what they must or must not do, made by the government of a city, state, nation, etc. [the *law* of the land].

lawn (lôn) *n.* ground covered with grass that is cut short, as around a house.

leaf (lēf) *n.* **1** any of the flat, green parts growing from the stem of a plant or tree. **2** a sheet of paper in a book [Each side of a *leaf* is a page.] —*pl.* **leaves** —**leaf′less** *adj.*

learn (lurn) *v.* **1** to get some knowledge or skill, as by studying or being taught [I have *learned* to knit. Some people never *learn* from experience.] **2** to find out about something; come to know [When did you *learn* of his illness?] **3** to fix in the mind; memorize [*Learn* this poem by tomorrow.] —**learned** (lurnd) or **learnt** (lurnt), **learn′ing**

least (lēst) *adj.* smallest in size, amount, or importance [I haven't the *least* interest in the matter.] ◆ *adv.* in the smallest amount or degree [I was *least* impressed by the music.] ◆ *n.* the smallest in amount, degree, etc. [The *least* you can do is apologize. I'm not in the *least* interested.]

leave (lēv) *v.* to go away or go from [Rosa *left* early. Jose *leaves* the house at 8:00.] —**left, leav′ing**

leaves (lēvz) *n. plural of* **leaf**.

left¹ (left) *adj.* on or to the side that is toward the west when one faces north [the *left* hand; a *left* turn]. ◆*n.* the left side [Forks are placed at the *left* of the plate.] ◆*adv.* on or toward the left hand or side [Turn *left* here.]

left² (left) *past tense and past participle of* **leave**.

lem·on (lem′ən) *n.* a small citrus fruit with a yellow skin and a juicy, sour pulp, used to make drinks or to flavor foods.

lens (lenz) *n.* 1 a piece of clear glass, plastic, etc., curved on one or both sides so as to bring together or spread rays of light that pass through it. Lenses are used in eyeglasses, cameras, microscopes, etc. 2 a clear part of the eye that focuses light rays on the retina.

lev·el (lev′'l) *adj.* with no part higher than any other part; flat and even [a *level* plain]. ◆*n.* a small tube of liquid in a frame that is placed on a surface to see if the surface is level. A bubble in the liquid moves to the center of the tube when the frame is level. ◆*v.* to make level or flat [to *level* ground with a bulldozer]. —**lev′eled** or **lev′elled, lev′el·ing** or **lev′el·ling**

lie¹ (lī) *v.* 1 to stretch one's body in a flat position along the ground, a bed, etc. 2 to be in a flat position; rest [A book is *lying* on the table.] —**lay, lain, ly′ing**

lie² (lī) *n.* something said that is not true, especially if it is said on purpose to fool or trick someone. ◆*v.* to tell a lie; say what is not true. —**lied, ly′ing**

life (līf) *n.* 1 the quality of plants and animals that makes it possible for them to take in food, grow, produce others of their kind, etc., and that makes them different from rocks, water, etc. [Death is the loss of *life*.] 2 a living thing; especially, a human being [The crash took six *lives*.] 3 the time that a person or thing is alive or lasts [Her *life* has just begun. What is the *life* of a battery?] —*pl.* **lives**

light¹ (līt) *n.* 1 brightness or radiance [the *light* of a candle; the *light* of love in his eyes]. 2 something that gives light, as a lamp [Turn off the *light*.] 3 a flame or spark to start something burning [a *light* for a pipe]. ◆*adj.* 1 having light; not dark [It's getting *light* outside.] 2 having a pale color; fair [*light* hair]. ◆*adv.* not brightly; in a pale way [a *light* green dress]. ◆*v.* to set on fire or catch fire; burn [to *light* a match; the candle *lighted* at once]. —**light′ed** or **lit, light′ing** —**light′ness** *n.*

light² (līt) *adj.* having little weight, especially for its size; not heavy [a *light* cargo; a *light* suit].

line (līn) *n.* 1 a cord, rope, string, etc. [a fishing *line*; a clothes*line*]. 2 a long, thin mark [*lines* made by a pen or pencil; *lines* formed in the face by wrinkles]. 3 a row of persons or things [a *line* of people waiting to get in; a *line* of words across a page]. ◆*v.* to form a line along [Elms *line* the streets.] —**lined, lin′ing**

lit·tle (lit′'l) *adj.* small in size; not large or big [a *little* house]. —**lit′tler** or **less** or **less′er, lit′tlest** or **least** ◆*adv.* to a small degree; not very much [She is a *little* better.] —**less, least** ◆*n.* a small amount [Have a *little* of this cake.] —**lit′tle·ness** *n.*

live¹ (liv) *v.* 1 to have life; be alive [No one *lives* forever.] 2 to make one's home; reside [We *live* on a farm.] —**lived, liv′ing**

live² (līv) *adj.* 1 having life; not dead. 2 that is broadcast while it is taking place; not photographed or recorded [a *live* television or radio program].

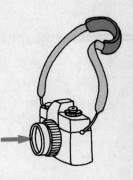

lens

a	ask, fat
ā	ape, date
ä	car, lot
e	elf, ten
er	berry, care
ē	even, meet
i	is, hit
ir	mirror, here
ī	ice, fire
ō	open, go
ô	law, horn
oi	oil, point
oo	look, pull
ōō	ooze, tool
yoo	unite, cure
yōō	cute, few
ou	out, crowd
u	up, cut
ʉr	fur, fern
ə	a in ago
	e in agent
	e in father
	i in unity
	o in collect
	u in focus
ch	chin, arch
ng	ring, singer
sh	she, dash
th	thin, truth
th	then, father
zh	s in pleasure
′	as in (ā′b'l)

liv·ing (liv′ing) *adj.* having life; alive; not dead. ◆*n.* **1** the fact of being alive. **2** the means of supporting oneself or one's family [He makes a *living* selling shoes.]

load (lōd) *n.* something that is carried or to be carried at one time [a heavy *load* on his back]. ◆*v.* to put something to be carried into or upon a carrier [to *load* a bus with passengers; to *load* groceries into a cart]. —**load′er** *n.*

loaf (lōf) *n.* **1** a portion of bread baked in one piece, usually oblong in shape. **2** any food baked in this shape [a meat *loaf*]. —*pl.* **loaves**

☆**loaf·er** (lōf′ər) *n.* **Loafer,** *a trademark for* a sport shoe somewhat like a moccasin.

loan (lōn) *n.* **1** the act of lending [Thanks for the *loan* of your pen.] **2** something lent, especially a sum of money. ◆*v.* to lend, especially a sum of money or something to be returned.

loaves (lōvz) *n.* *plural of* **loaf.**

long[1] (lông) *adj.* **1** measuring much from end to end or from beginning to end; not short [a *long* board; a *long* trip; a *long* wait]. **2** taking a longer time to say than other sounds [The "a" in "cave" and the "i" in "hide" are *long*.] ◆*adv.* for a long time [Don't be gone *long*.]

long[2] (lông) *v.* to want very much; feel a strong desire for [We *long* to go home.]

loose (lōōs) *adj.* **1** not tied or held back; free [a *loose* end of wire]. **2** not tight or firmly fastened on or in something [*loose* clothing; a *loose* table leg]. ◆*adv.* in a loose way [My coat hangs *loose*.] —**loose′ly** *adv.* —**loose′ness** *n.*

Los An·gel·es (lôs an′jə ləs *or* lôs ang′gə ləs) a city on the southwestern coast of California.

Los Angeles

lost (lôst) *past tense and past participle of* **lose.** ◆*adj.* that is mislaid, missing, destroyed, defeated, wasted, etc. [a *lost* hat; a *lost* child; a *lost* ship; a *lost* cause; *lost* time].

loud (loud) *adj.* **1** strong in sound; not soft or quiet [a *loud* noise; a *loud* bell]. **2** noisy [a *loud* party]. ◆*adv.* in a loud way. —**loud′ly** *adv.* —**loud′ness** *n.*

love·ly (luv′lē) *adj.* **1** very pleasing in looks or character; beautiful [a *lovely* person]. **2** very enjoyable: *used only in everyday talk* [We had a *lovely* time.] —**love′li·er, love′li·est** —**love′li·ness** *n.*

loy·al (loi′əl) *adj.* **1** faithful to one's country [a *loyal* citizen]. **2** faithful to one's family, duty, beliefs, etc. [a *loyal* friend; a *loyal* member]. —**loy′al·ly** *adv.*

Mm

made (mād) *past tense and past participle of* **make.** ◆*adj.* built; put together; formed [a well-*made* house].

mag·ic (maj′ik) *n.* **1** the use of charms, spells, and rituals that are supposed to make things happen in an unnatural way [In fairy tales, *magic* is used to work miracles.] **2** the skill of doing puzzling tricks by moving the hands so fast as to fool those watching and by using boxes with false bottoms, hidden strings, etc.; sleight of hand. ◆*adj.* of or as if by magic.

maid (mād) *n.* **1** a maiden. **2** a girl or woman servant.

mail (māl) *n.* **1** letters, packages, etc., carried and delivered by a post office. **2** the system of picking up and delivering letters, papers, etc.; postal system [Send it by *mail*.] ◆*adj.* having to do with or carrying mail [a *mail* truck]. ◆*v.* ☆to send by mail; place in a mailbox. —**mail′a·ble** *adj.*

Maine (mān) a New England state of the U.S.: abbreviated **Me.**, **ME**

make (māk) *v.* **1** to bring into being; build, create, produce, put together, etc. [to *make* a dress; to *make* a fire; to *make* plans; to *make* noise]. **2** to do, perform, carry on, etc. [to *make* a right turn; to *make* a speech]. —**made, mak′ing**

man (man) *n.* **1** an adult male human being. **2** any human being; person ["that all *men* are created equal"]. **3** the human race; mankind [*man's* conquest of space]. —*pl.* **men**

mark (märk) *n.* **1** a spot, stain, scratch, dent, etc., made on a surface. **2** a printed or written sign or label [punctuation *marks*; a trade*mark*]. **3** a grade or rating [a *mark* of B in spelling]. ◆*v.* **1** to make a mark or marks on. **2** to draw or write [*Mark* your name on your gym shoes.] **3** to give a grade to [to *mark* test papers].

mar·ry (mar′ē) *v.* **1** to join a man and a woman as husband and wife [A ship's captain may *marry* people at sea.] **2** to take as one's husband or wife [John Alden *married* Priscilla.] —**mar′ried, mar′ry·ing**

may (mā) *a helping verb used with other verbs and meaning:* **1** to be possible or likely [It *may* rain.] **2** to be allowed or have permission [You *may* go.] **3** to be able to as a result [Be quiet so that we *may* hear.] *May* is also used in exclamations to mean "I or we hope or wish" [*May* you win!] —The past tense is **might.**

may·be (mā′bē) *adv.* it may be; perhaps.

mel·o·dy (mel′ə dē) *n.* **1** an arrangement of musical tones in a series so as to form a tune; often, the main tune in the harmony of a musical piece [The *melody* is played by the oboes.] **2** any pleasing series of sounds [a *melody* sung by birds]. —*pl.* **mel′o·dies**

melt (melt) *v.* **1** to change from a solid to a liquid, as by heat [The bacon fat *melted* in the frying pan.] **2** to dissolve [The candy *melted* in my mouth.]

men (men) *n.* *plural of* **man.**

mice (mīs) *n.* *plural of* **mouse.**

Mich·i·gan (mish′ə gən) **1** a state in the north central part of the U.S.: abbreviated **Mich.**, **MI 2** one of the Great Lakes, west of Lake Huron: *the full name is* **Lake Michigan.**

might[1] (mīt) *past tense of* **may.**

might[2] (mīt) *n.* great strength, force, or power [Pull with all your *might*.]

Mis·sis·sip·pi (mis′ə sip′ē) **1** a river in the U.S., flowing from Minnesota to the Gulf of Mexico. **2** a state in the southeastern part of the U.S.: abbreviated **Miss.**, **MS.**

mon·ey (mun′ē) *n.* coins of gold, silver, or other metal, or paper bills to take the place of these, issued by a government for use in buying and selling. —*pl.* **mon′eys** or **mon′ies**

moon·beam (mōōn′bēm) *n.* a ray of moonlight.

moon·light (mōōn′līt) *n.* the light of the moon.

morn·ing (môr′niŋ) *n.* the early part of the day, from midnight to noon or, especially, from dawn to noon.

money

a	ask, fat
ā	ape, date
ä	car, lot
e	elf, ten
er	berry, care
ē	even, meet
i	is, hit
ir	mirror, here
ī	ice, fire
ō	open, go
ô	law, horn
oi	oil, point
oo	look, pull
ōō	ooze, tool
yoo	unite, cure
yōō	cute, few
ou	out, crowd
u	up, cut
ur	fur, fern
ə	a in ago
	e in agent
	e in father
	i in unity
	o in collect
	u in focus
ch	chin, arch
ŋ	ring, singer
sh	she, dash
th	thin, truth
th	then, father
zh	s in pleasure
′	as in (ā′b'l)

most·ly (mōst′lē) *adv.* mainly; chiefly.

☆**mo·tel** (mō tel′) *n.* a hotel for those traveling by car, usually with a parking area easily reached from each room.

mouse (mous) *n.* **1** a small, gnawing animal found in houses and fields throughout the world. **2** a timid person. ☆**3** a small device moved by hand, as on a flat surface, so as to make the cursor move on a computer terminal screen. —*pl.* **mice** (mīs)

mouse

muf·fler (muf′lər) *n.* **1** a scarf worn around the throat for warmth. **2** a thing used to deaden noise, as ☆a part fastened to the exhaust pipe of an automobile engine.

mul·ti·ply (mul′tə plī) *v.* **1** to become more, greater, etc.; increase [Our troubles *multiplied*.] **2** to repeat a certain figure a certain number of times [If you *multiply* 10 by 4, or repeat 10 four times, you get the product 40.] —**mul′ti·plied, mul′ti·ply·ing**

mu·sic (myoo′zik) *n.* **1** the art of putting tones together in various melodies, rhythms, and harmonies to form compositions for singing or playing on instruments [She teaches *music*.] **2** any series of pleasing sounds [the *music* of birds].

must·n't (mus′′nt) must not.

needle

my·self (mī self′) *pron.* **1** my own self. *This form of* I *is used when the object is the same as the subject of the verb* [I hurt *myself*.] **2** my usual or true self [I'm not *myself* today.] *Myself is also used to give force to the subject* [I'll do it *myself*.]

nee·dle (nē′d′l) *n.* **1** a small, slender piece of steel with a sharp point and a hole for thread, used for sewing. **2** a short, slender piece of metal, often tipped with diamond, that moves in the grooves of a phonograph record to pick up the vibrations. **3** the thin, pointed leaf of a pine, spruce, etc. **4** the sharp, very slender metal tube at the end of a hypodermic syringe.

New York (yôrk) **1** a state in the northeastern part of the U.S.: abbreviated **N.Y., NY 2** a seaport in southeastern New York State, on the Atlantic Ocean; the largest city in the U.S.: *often called* **New York City.**

next (nekst) *adj.* coming just before or just after; nearest or closest [the *next* person in line; the *next* room; *next* Monday]. ◆*adv.* **1** in the nearest place, time, etc. [She sits *next* to me in school. Please wait on me *next*.] **2** at the first chance after this [What should I do *next*?]

nice (nīs) *adj.* good, pleasant, agreeable, pretty, kind, polite, etc.: *used as a general word showing that one likes something* [a *nice* time; a *nice* dress; a *nice* neighbor]. —**nic′er, nic′est** —**nice′ly** *adv.*

night (nīt) *n.* the time of darkness between sunset and sunrise. ◆*adj.* of, for, or at night [*night* school].

nine (nīn) *n., adj.* one more than eight; the number 9.

ninth (nīnth) *adj.* coming after eight others; 9th in order. ◆*n.* one of nine equal parts of something; 1/9.

noise (noiz) **n.** sound, especially a loud, harsh, or confused sound [the *noise* of fireworks; *noises* of a city street]. ◆**v.** to make public by telling; spread [to *noise* a rumor about]. —**noised, nois'ing**

nois·y (noi'zē) **adj.** **1** making noise [a *noisy* bell]. **2** full of noise [a *noisy* theater]. —**nois'i·er, nois'i·est** —**nois'i·ly adv.** —**nois'i·ness n.**

note (nōt) **n.** **1** a word, phrase, or sentence written down to help one remember something one has heard, read, thought, etc. [The students kept *notes* on the lecture.] **2** a short letter. **3** close attention; notice [Take *note* of what I say.] **4** a musical tone; also, the symbol for such a tone, showing how long it is to be sounded. Where it is placed on the staff tells how high or low it is.

noun (noun) **n.** a word that is the name of a person, thing, action, quality, etc. A phrase or a clause can be used in a sentence as a noun ["Boy," "water," and "truth" are *nouns*.]

No·vem·ber (nō vem'bər) **n.** the eleventh month of the year, which has 30 days: abbreviated **Nov.**

nurse (nʉrs) **n.** a person who has been trained to take care of sick people, help doctors, etc. ◆**v.** to take care of sick people, as a nurse does. —**nursed, nurs'ing**

Oo

ob·ject (äb'jikt) **n.** **1** a thing that can be seen or touched; something that takes up space [That brown *object* is a purse.] **2** a person or thing toward which one turns one's thoughts, feelings, or actions [the *object* of my affection].

Oc·to·ber (äk tō'bər) **n.** the tenth month of the year, which has 31 days: abbreviated **Oct.**

O·hi·o (ō hī'ō) **1** a state in the north central part of the U.S.: abbreviated **O., OH 2** a river that flows along the southern borders of Ohio, Indiana, and Illinois to the Mississippi. —**O·hi·o·an adj., n.**

oint·ment (oint'mənt) **n.** an oily cream rubbed on the skin to heal it or make it soft and smooth; salve.

once (wuns) **adv.** **1** one time [We eat together *once* a week.] **2** at some time in the past; formerly [They were rich *once*.] ◆**conj.** as soon as; whenever [*Once* the horse tires, it will quit.] ◆**n.** one time [I'll go this *once*.]

on·ly (ōn'lē) **adj.** without any other or others of the same kind; sole [the *only* suit I own; their *only* friends]. ◆**adv.** and no other; and no more; just; merely [I have *only* fifty cents. Bite off *only* what you can chew.]

or·der (ôr'dər) **n.** **1** the way in which things are placed or follow one another; arrangement [The entries in this dictionary are in alphabetical *order*.] **2** a direction telling someone what to do, given by a person with authority; command [The general's *orders* were quickly obeyed.] **3** a request for something that one wants to buy or receive [Mail your *order* for flower seeds today.] ◆**v.** **1** to tell what to do; give an order to [The captain *ordered* the troops to charge.] **2** to ask for something one wants to buy or receive [Please *order* some art supplies for the class.]

our (our) **pron.** of us or done by us. *This possessive form of* **we** *is used before a noun and thought of as an adjective* [*our* car; *our* work].

a	ask, fat
ā	ape, date
ä	car, lot
e	elf, ten
er	berry, care
ē	even, meet
i	is, hit
ir	mirror, here
ī	ice, fire
ō	open, go
ô	law, horn
oi	oil, point
oo	look, pull
ōo	ooze, tool
yoo	unite, cure
yōo	cute, few
ou	out, crowd
u	up, cut
ʉr	fur, fern
ə	a in ago
	e in agent
	e in father
	i in unity
	o in collect
	u in focus
ch	chin, arch
ŋ	ring, singer
sh	she, dash
th	thin, truth
th	then, father
zh	s in pleasure
'	as in (ā'b'l)

ox

oxford

our·selves (our selvz′) *pron.* **1** our own selves. *This form of* **we** *is used when the object is the same as the subject of the verb* [We hurt *ourselves*.] **2** our usual or true selves [We are not *ourselves* today.] *Ourselves* is also used to give force to the subject [We built it *ourselves*.]

ox (äks) *n.* any animal of a group that chew their cud and have cloven hoofs, including the buffalo, bison, etc. —*pl.* **ox·en** (äk′s'n)

ox·ford (äks′fərd) *n.* a low shoe that is laced over the instep: *also called* **oxford shoe**.

page¹ (pāj) *n.* one side of a leaf of paper in a book, newspaper, letter, etc. ◆*v.* to turn pages in looking quickly [to *page* through a book]. —**paged, pag′ing**

page² (pāj) *n.* a boy, or sometimes a girl, who runs errands and carries messages in a hotel, office building, or legislature. ◆*v.* ☆to try to find a person by calling out the name, as a hotel page does. —**paged, pag′ing**

pair (per) *n.* **1** two things of the same kind that are used together; set of two [a *pair* of skates]. **2** a single thing with two parts that are used together [a *pair* of eyeglasses; a *pair* of pants]. ◆*v.* to arrange in or form a pair or pairs; match.

pan·try (pan′trē) *n.* a small room near the kitchen where food, dishes, pots, etc., are kept. —*pl.* **pan′tries**

☆**pants** (pants) *n.pl.* a garment reaching from the waist to the ankles or the knees and covering each leg separately; trousers.

pa·per (pā′pər) *n.* **1** a thin material in sheets, made from wood pulp, rags, etc., and used to write or print on, to wrap or decorate with, etc. **2** a single sheet of this material. **3** something written or printed on paper, as an essay, report, etc. [The teacher is grading a set of *papers*.]

pa·rade (pə rād′) *n.* any march or procession, as to celebrate a holiday [a Fourth of July *parade*]. ◆*v.* to march in a parade. —**pa·rad′ed, pa·rad′ing**

pare (per) *v.* to cut or trim away the rind or covering of something; peel [to *pare* a potato; to *pare* the bark from a tree]. —**pared, par′ing**

par·ty (pär′tē) *n.* **1** a gathering of people to have a good time [a birthday *party*]. **2** a group of people working or acting together [a hunting *party*]. —*pl.* **par′ties**

past (past) *adj.* gone by; ended; over [What is *past* is finished.] ◆*n.* the time that has gone by [That's all in the *past*.] ◆*prep.* later than or farther than; beyond [ten minutes *past* two; *past* the city limits].

patch (pach) *n.* **1** a piece of cloth, metal, etc., put on to mend a hole, tear, or worn spot. **2** a bandage put on a wound or a pad worn over an injured eye. **3** an area or spot [*patches* of blue sky]. ◆*v.* to put a patch or patches on [to *patch* the worn elbows of a coat].

pear (per) *n.* a soft, juicy fruit, often yellow or green, that is round at one end and narrows toward the stem.

peo·ple (pē′p'l) *n.* human beings; persons.

per·haps (pər haps′) *adv.* possibly; maybe [*Perhaps* it will rain. Did you, *perhaps*, lose it?]

pe·ri·od (pir′ē əd) *n.* **1** the time that goes by during which something goes on, a cycle is repeated, etc. [the medieval *period*; a *period* of hot weather]. **2** the mark of punctuation (.) used at the end of most sentences or often after abbreviations.

per·son (pur′s'n) *n.* a human being; man, woman, or child [every *person* in this room].

☆**phone** (fōn) *n., v.* a shorter word for **telephone**: *used only in everyday talk.* —**phoned, phon′ing**

pick¹ (pik) *n.* a heavy metal tool with a pointed head, used for breaking up rock, soil, etc.

pick² (pik) *v.* **1** to choose or select [The judges *picked* the winner.] **2** to scratch or dig at with the fingers or with something pointed [to *pick* the teeth with a toothpick]. **3** to pluck or gather with the fingers or hands [to *pick* flowers]. ◆*n.* the act of choosing or the thing chosen; choice [Take your *pick* of these books.] —**pick′er** *n.*

pinch (pinch) *v.* to squeeze between a finger and the thumb or between two surfaces [He gently *pinched* the baby's cheek. She *pinched* her finger in the door.] ◆*n.* **1** a pinching; squeeze; nip [a *pinch* on the arm]. **2** the amount that can be picked up between the finger and thumb [a *pinch* of salt].

pitch (pich) *v.* **1** to throw or toss [*Pitch* the newspaper on the porch.] **2** to set up; make ready for use [to *pitch* a tent]. **3** to slope downward [The roof *pitches* sharply.] ◆*n.* **1** anything pitched or thrown [The wild *pitch* hit the batter.] **2** the highness or lowness of a musical sound [Some notes have a *pitch* too high for human ears to hear.]

place (plās) *n.* **1** a space taken up or used by a person or thing [Please take your *places*.] **2** a house, apartment, etc., where one lives [Visit me at my *place*.] **3** rank or position, especially in a series [I finished the race in fifth *place*.] ◆*v.* **1** to put in a certain place, position, etc. [*Place* the pencil on the desk.] **2** to finish in a certain position in a contest [Lynn *placed* sixth in the race.] —**placed, plac′ing**

plan (plan) *n.* **1** a method or way of doing something that has been thought out ahead of time [vacation *plans*]. **2** a drawing that shows how the parts of a building or piece of ground are arranged [floor *plans* of a house; a *plan* of the battlefield]. ◆*v.* **1** to think out a way of making or doing something [They *planned* their escape carefully.] **2** to make a drawing or diagram of beforehand [An architect is *planning* our new school.] **3** to have in mind; intend [I *plan* to visit Hawaii soon.] —**planned, plan′ning**

plan·et (plan′it) *n.* any of the large heavenly bodies that revolve around the sun and shine as they reflect the sun's light. The planets, in their order from the sun, are Mercury, Venus, Earth, Mars, Jupiter, Saturn, Uranus, Neptune, and Pluto. —**plan·e·tar·y** (plan′ə ter′ē) *adj.*

plant (plant) *n.* **1** any living thing that cannot move about by itself, has no sense organs, and usually makes its own food by photosynthesis [Trees, shrubs, and vegetables are *plants*.] **2** the machinery, buildings, etc., of a factory or business. ◆*v.* to put into the ground so that it will grow [to *plant* corn].

pick

a	ask, fat
ā	ape, date
ä	car, lot
e	elf, ten
er	berry, care
ē	even, meet
i	is, hit
ir	mirror, here
ī	ice, fire
ō	open, go
ô	law, horn
oi	oil, point
oo	look, pull
o͞o	ooze, tool
yoo	unite, cure
yo͞o	cute, few
ou	out, crowd
u	up, cut
ur	fur, fern
ə	a in ago
	e in agent
	e in father
	i in unity
	o in collect
	u in focus
ch	chin, arch
ng	ring, singer
sh	she, dash
th	thin, truth
th	then, father
zh	s in pleasure
′	as in (ā′b'l)

poison ivy

play (plā) **v.** **1** to have fun; amuse oneself [children *playing* in the sand]. **2** to do in fun [to *play* a joke on a friend]. **3** to take part in a game or sport [to *play* golf]. **4** to perform music on [He *plays* the piano.] **5** to give out sounds: said of a phonograph, tape recorder, etc. ◆**n.** **1** something done just for fun or to amuse oneself; recreation [She has little time for *play*.] **2** fun; joking [Jan said it in *play*.] **3** the playing of a game [Rain halted *play*.] **4** a story that is acted out, as on a stage, on radio or television, etc.; drama.

play·ful (plā'fəl) **adj.** **1** fond of play or fun; lively; frisky [a *playful* puppy]. **2** said or done in fun; joking [She gave her brother a *playful* shove.] —**play'ful·ly adv.** —**play'ful·ness n.**

please (plēz) **v.** **1** to give pleasure to; satisfy [Few things *please* me more than a good book.] **2** to be kind enough to: *used in asking for something politely* [*Please* pass the salt.] **3** to wish or desire; like [Do as you *please*.] —**pleased, pleas'ing**

plen·ty (plen'tē) **n.** a supply that is large enough; all that is needed [We have *plenty* of help.]

plumb·er (plum'ər) **n.** a person whose work is putting in and repairing the pipes and fixtures of water and gas systems in a building.

potato

point (point) **n.** **1** a position or place; location [the *point* where the roads meet]. **2** a dot in printing or writing [a decimal *point*]. **3** a unit used in measuring or scoring [A touchdown is worth six *points*.] **4** a sharp end [the *point* of a needle]. **5** an important or main idea or fact [the *point* of a joke]. ◆**v.** to aim one's finger [He *pointed* to the book he wanted.]

☆**poison ivy** **1** a plant with whitish berries and with leaves that grow in groups of three. It can cause a skin rash if touched. **2** a rash caused by this plant.

☆**poison oak** *another name for* **poison ivy** *or* **poison sumac.**

pol·len (päl'ən) **n.** the yellow powder found on the stamens of flowers. It is made up of male cells which fertilize another flower when carried to its pistil, as by bees or the wind.

pool[1] (pōōl) **n.** **1** a small pond. **2** a puddle. **3** *a shorter form of* **swimming pool.**

pool[2] (pōōl) **n.** a game of billiards played on a table, called a **pool table,** having six pockets into which the balls are knocked.

po·ta·to (pə tā'tō) **n.** a plant whose tuber, or thick, starchy underground stem, is used as a vegetable. —*pl.* **po·ta'toes**

pound[1] (pound) **n.** a unit of weight, equal to 16 ounces in avoirdupois weight or 12 ounces in troy weight. One pound avoirdupois equals 453.59 grams.

pound[2] (pound) **v.** **1** to hit with many heavy blows; hit hard [to *pound* on a door]. **2** to beat in a heavy way; throb [Her heart *pounded* from the exercise.] ◆**n.** a hard blow or the sound of it.

pound[3] (pound) **n.** a closed-in place for keeping animals, especially stray ones [a dog *pound*].

pow·er (pou'ər) **n.** **1** ability to do or act [Lobsters have the *power* to grow new claws.] **2** strength or force [the *power* of a boxer's blows]. **3** force or energy that can be put to work [electric *power*]. **4** the ability to control others; authority [the *power* of the law]. ◆**adj.** worked by electricity or other kind of power [a *power* saw].

pray (prā) **v.** **1** to talk or recite a set of words to God in worship or in asking for something. **2** to beg or ask for seriously ["*Pray* tell me" means "I beg you to tell me."]

pret·ty (prit′ē *or* pʉr′tē) **adj.** pleasant to look at or hear, especially in a delicate, dainty, or graceful way [a *pretty* girl; a *pretty* voice; a *pretty* garden]. —**pret′ti·er, pret′ti·est** ◆**adv.** somewhat; rather [I'm *pretty* tired.] ◆**v.** to make pretty [She *prettied* up her room.] —**pret′tied, pret′ty·ing** —**pret′ti·ly adv.** —**pret′ti·ness n.**

prize (prīz) **n.** **1** something offered or given to a winner of a contest, lottery, etc. [The first *prize* is a bicycle.] **2** anything worth trying to get [Her friendship would be a great *prize*.]

proud (proud) **adj.** **1** having proper respect for oneself, one's work, one's family, etc. [He is too *proud* to ask for help.] **2** thinking too highly of oneself; conceited; vain or haughty [They are too *proud* to say hello to us.] **3** feeling or causing pride or pleasure [his *proud* mother; a *proud* moment]. —**proud′ly adv.**

pud·dle (pud′'l) **n.** a small pool of water or water mixed with earth [*puddles* after the rain; a mud *puddle*].

pu·pil (pyo͞o′p'l) **n.** **1** a person being taught by a teacher, as in a school; student. **2** the dark opening in the center of the eye that grows larger or smaller to let in more or less light.

pup·py (pup′ē) **n.** a young dog. —*pl.* **pup′pies**

push (poosh) **v.** **1** to press against so as to move; shove [to *push* a stalled car; to *push* a stake into the ground]. **2** to urge the use, sale, etc., of [The company is *pushing* its new product.] ◆**n.** the act of pushing; a shove or thrust [One hard *push* opened the door.]

quite (kwīt) **adv.** **1** completely; entirely [I haven't *quite* finished eating.] **2** really; truly [You are *quite* a musician.] **3** very or somewhat [It's *quite* warm outside.]

race (rās) **n.** a contest, as among runners, swimmers, cars, boats, etc., to see who can go fastest. ◆**v.** **1** to take part in a race [How many planes are *racing*?] **2** to have a race with [I'll *race* you to the corner.] **3** to go very fast [Her eye *raced* over the page.] —**raced, rac′ing**

rain (rān) **n.** **1** water that falls to the earth in drops formed from the moisture in the air. **2** the falling of such drops; a shower [Sunshine followed the *rain*.] ◆**v.** to fall as rain [It is *raining*.]

☆**rain·coat** (rān′kōt) **n.** a waterproof coat that protects a person from the rain.

raise (rāz) **v.** **1** to cause to rise; lift [*Raise* your hand if you have a question. *Raise* the window.] **2** to make larger, greater, higher, louder, etc. [to *raise* prices; to *raise* one's voice]. **3** to bring up; take care of; support [to *raise* a family]. —**raised, rais′ing** ◆**n.** a making or becoming larger; especially, an increase in salary or wages.

rash (rash) **n.** a breaking out of red spots on the skin [The measles gave her a *rash*.]

re- *a prefix meaning:* **1** again [To *reappear* is to appear again.] **2** back [To *repay* is to pay back.]

a	ask, fat
ā	ape, date
ä	car, lot
e	elf, ten
er	berry, care
ē	even, meet
i	is, hit
ir	mirror, here
ī	ice, fire
ō	open, go
ô	law, horn
oi	oil, point
o͞o	look, pull
o͞o	ooze, tool
yo͞o	unite, cure
yo͞o	cute, few
ou	out, crowd
u	up, cut
ʉr	fur, fern
ə	a in ago
	e in agent
	e in father
	i in unity
	o in collect
	u in focus
ch	chin, arch
ŋ	ring, singer
sh	she, dash
th	thin, truth
th	then, father
zh	s in pleasure
′	as in (ā′b'l)

read¹ (rēd) *v.* **1** to get the meaning of something written or printed by understanding its letters, signs, or numbers [I *read* the book. She *read* the gas meter. Can you *read* music?] **2** to speak printed or written words aloud [*Read* the story to me.] —**read** (red), **read′ing**

read² (red) *past tense and past participle of* **read¹**. ◆*adj.* having knowledge got from reading; informed [They are both well-*read*.]

read·y (red′ē) *adj.* prepared to act or to be used at once [Is everyone *ready* to leave? Your bath is *ready*.] —**read′i·er, read′i·est** ◆*v.* to prepare [to *ready* the house for guests.] —**read′ied, read′y·ing** —**read′i·ness** *n.*

re·build (rē bild′) *v.* to build again, especially something that was damaged, ruined, etc. —**re·built′, re·build′ing**

re·do (rē doo) *v.* **1** to do again **2** to redecorate, as a room. —**re·did′, re·done′, re·do′ing**

re·fill (rē fil′) *v.* to fill again. ◆*n.* (re′fil) **1** something to refill a special container [a *refill* for a ballpoint pen]. **2** any extra filling of a prescription for medicine. —**re·fill′a·ble** *adj.*

re·form (ri fôrm′) *v.* **1** to make better by getting rid of faults, wrongs, etc.; improve [to *reform* working conditions in a factory; to *reform* a criminal]. **2** to become better; give up one's bad ways [The outlaw *reformed* and became a better citizen.] ◆*n.* correction of faults or evils, as in government.

re·fresh (ri fresh′) *v.* to make fresh again; bring back into good condition [A soft rain *refreshed* the wilted plants. She *refreshed* herself with a short nap. *Refresh* my memory by playing the piece again.]

re·mind (ri mīnd′) *v.* to make remember or think of [*Remind* me to pay the gas bill.]

re·name (rē nām′) *v.* to give a new or different name to [Ceylon was *renamed* Sri Lanka.] —**re·named′, re·nam′ing**

re·new (ri noo′ *or* ri nyoo′) *v.* **1** to make new or fresh again; restore [*Renew* that old table by painting it.] **2** to give or get again for a new period of time [It is time to *renew* your subscription.] —**re·new′al** *n.*

re·pay (ri pā′) *v.* **1** to pay back [to *repay* a loan]. **2** to do or give something to someone in return for some favor, service, etc., received [to *repay* a kindness]. —**re·paid′, re·pay′ing** —**re·pay′ment** *n.*

re·place (ri plās′) *v.* **1** to put back in the right place [*Replace* the tools on my bench when you are through.] **2** to take the place of [Many workers have been *replaced* by computers.] **3** to put another in the place of one used, lost, broken, etc. [to *replace* a worn tire]. —**re·placed′, re·plac′ing**

re·ply (ri plī′) *v.* to answer by saying or doing something [to *reply* to a question; to *reply* to the enemy's fire with a counter-attack]. —**re·plied′, re·ply′ing** ◆*n.* an answer. —*pl.* **re·plies′**

re·run (rē run′) *v.* to run again. —**re·ran′, re·run′ning** ◆*n.* (rē′run) ☆ a repeat showing of a movie, taped TV program, etc.

re·sort (ri zôrt′) *v.* to turn for help [It would be wrong to *resort* to force to gain our end.] ◆*n.* a place where many people go, as for a vacation [a winter *resort* for skiing].

ret·i·na (ret′'n ə) *n.* the part at the back of the eyeball, made up of special cells that react to light. The image picked up by the lens of the eye is formed on the retina.

re·triev·er (ri trēv′ər) *n.* a dog that is trained to retrieve game in hunting.

re·write (rē rīt′) *v.* to write again or in different words; revise [to *rewrite* a story]. —**re·wrote′, re·writ′ten, re·writ′ing**

rich (rich) *adj.* **1** having wealth; owning much money or property; wealthy. **2** having much of something; well supplied [Tomatoes are *rich* in vitamin C.] **3** full of fats, or fats and sugar [*rich* foods]. —**rich′ly** *adv.* —**rich′ness** *n.*

ring¹ (ring) *v.* **1** to cause a bell to sound [*Ring* the doorbell.] **2** to make the sound of a bell [The phone *rang*.] —**rang** or rarely **rung, rung, ring′ing** ◆*n.* **1** the sound of a bell. **2** a telephone call [Give me a *ring* soon.] —**ring′er** *n.*

ring² (ring) *n.* **1** a thin band of metal, plastic, etc., shaped like a circle and worn on the finger or used to hold or fasten things [a wedding *ring*; a curtain *ring*]. **2** a line or edge forming a circle [a *ring* around the moon]. **3** an enclosed space for contests, shows, etc. [the *ring* of a circus; a boxing *ring*]. ◆*v.* to make a circle around or form in a ring. —**ringed, ring′ing** —**ringed** *adj.* —**ring′er** *n.*

Ri·o Grande (rē′ō grand′ *or* rē′ō gran′dē) a river that flows from Colorado to the Gulf of Mexico. It forms the boundary between Texas and Mexico.

rise (rīz) *v.* **1** to stand up or get up from a lying or sitting position. **2** to become greater, higher, or stronger [The temperature *rose*. Prices are *rising*. Her voice *rose*.] —**rose, ris′en, ris′ing** ◆*n.* **1** a piece of ground higher than that around it [There's a good view of the countryside from the top of the *rise*.] **2** the fact of becoming greater, higher, etc.; increase [a *rise* in prices].

rock¹ (räk) *n.* a large mass of stone.

rock² (räk) *v.* to move or swing back and forth or from side to side [to *rock* a cradle]. ◆*n.* a rocking movement.

roof (ro͞of *or* ro͝of) *n.* **1** the outside top covering of a building. **2** anything like a roof in the way it is placed or used [the *roof* of the mouth; the *roof* of a car]. —**roof′less** *adj.*

rough (ruf) *adj.* **1** not smooth or level; uneven [a *rough* road; *rough* fur]. **2** full of noise and wild action; disorderly [*rough* play]. **3** not gentle or mild, as in manners; rude, harsh, etc. [*rough* language]. **4** having little comfort or luxury [the *rough* life of a pioneer].

round (round) *adj.* shaped like a ball, a circle, or a tube; having an outline that forms a circle or curve [The world is *round*. Wheels are *round*. The ship has a *round* smokestack.] ◆*n.* a short song for two or more persons or groups, in which the second starts when the first gets to the second phrase, and so on.

rush (rush) *v.* **1** to move, send, take, etc., with great speed [I *rushed* from the room. We *rushed* him to a hospital.] **2** to act in haste, without thinking carefully [Don't *rush* into marriage.] ◆*adj.* that must be done or sent in a hurry [a *rush* order].

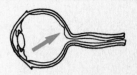

retina

a	ask, fat
ā	ape, date
ä	car, lot
e	elf, ten
er	berry, care
ē	even, meet
i	is, hit
ir	mirror, here
ī	ice, fire
ō	open, go
ô	law, horn
oi	oil, point
o͝o	look, pull
o͞o	ooze, tool
yo͞o	unite, cure
yo͞o	cute, few
ou	out, crowd
u	up, cut
ʉr	fur, fern
ə	**a** in ago
	e in agent
	e in father
	i in unity
	o in collect
	u in focus
ch	**ch**in, ar**ch**
ng	ri**ng**, si**ng**er
sh	**sh**e, da**sh**
th	**th**in, tru**th**
th	**th**en, fa**th**er
zh	**s** in pleasure
′	as in (ā′b'l)

Ss

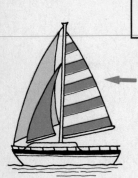

sail

said (sed) *past tense and past participle of* **say.** ◆*adj.* named or mentioned before [The *said* contract is no longer in force.]

sail (sāl) *n.* **1** a sheet of heavy cloth such as canvas, used on a ship or boat to move it by catching the wind. **2** a trip in a ship or boat, especially one moved by sails [Let's go for a *sail.*] ◆*v.* **1** to travel on water [This liner *sails* between Miami and New York.] **2** to move smoothly [a hawk *sailing* in the sky].

sale (sāl) *n.* **1** the act of selling, or exchanging something for money [The clerk made ten *sales* today.] **2** a special selling of goods at prices lower than usual [a clearance *sale*].

sam·ple (sam'p'l) *n.* a part or piece that shows what the whole group or thing is like; specimen or example [little pieces of wallpaper for *samples*; a *sample* of his typing]. ◆*adj.* that is a sample [a *sample* page of the book]. ◆*v.* to test by trying a sample [He *sampled* the basket of grapes.] —**sam'pled, sam'pling**

san·dal (san'd'l) *n.* **1** a kind of shoe that is just a flat sole fastened to the foot by straps. **2** a kind of open slipper or low shoe.

sandal

Sat·ur·day (sat'ər dē) *n.* the seventh and last day of the week.

sau·cer (sô'sər) *n.* **1** a small, shallow dish, especially one for a cup to rest on. **2** anything round and shallow like this dish.

save (sāv) *v.* **1** to rescue or keep from harm or danger [He was *saved* from drowning.] **2** to keep or store up for future use [She *saved* her money for a vacation.] —**saved, sav'ing** —**sav'er** *n.*

sav·ing (sā'viṇ) *n.* *often* **savings**, *pl.* a thing, amount, sum of money, etc., saved [a *saving* of 20%; one's life *savings*].

scale¹ (skāl) *n.* **1** a series of marks along a line, with regular spaces in-between, used for measuring [A Celsius thermometer has a basic *scale* of 100 degrees.] **2** the way that the size of a map, model, or drawing compares with the size of the thing that it stands for [One inch on a map of this *scale* equals 100 miles of real distance.] **3** a series of musical tones arranged in order from the highest to the lowest or from the lowest to the highest. —**on a large scale,** to a large extent.

scale² (skāl) *n.* any of the thin, flat, hard plates that cover and protect certain fish and reptiles.

scale³ (skāl) *n.* **1** either of the shallow pans of a balance. **2** *often* **scales**, *pl.* the balance itself; also, any device or machine for weighing.

school¹ (sko͞ol) *n.* **1** a place, usually a special building, for teaching and learning, as a public school, dancing school, college, etc. **2** the students and teachers of a school [an assembly for the whole *school*]. ◆*adj.* of or for a school or schools [our *school* band].

school² (sko͞ol) *n.* a large group of fish or water animals of the same kind swimming together [a *school* of porpoises]. ◆*v.* to swim together in a school.

sci·ence (sī'əns) *n.* knowledge made up of an orderly system of facts that have been learned from study, observation, and experiments [*Science* helps us to understand how things happen.]

scoop (skōōp) *n.* **1** a kitchen tool like a small shovel, used to take up sugar, flour, etc., or one with a small, round bowl for dishing up ice cream, etc. **2** the amount taken up at one time by a scoop [three *scoops* of ice cream]. ◆*v.* to take up as with a scoop [We *scooped* up water with our hands.]

scratch (skrach) *v.* **1** to mark or cut the surface of slightly with something sharp [Thorns *scratched* her legs. Our cat *scratched* the chair with its claws.] **2** to rub or scrape, as with the nails, to relieve itching [to *scratch* a mosquito bite]. **3** to cross out by drawing lines through [She *scratched* out what he had written.] ◆*n.* **1** a mark or cut made in a surface by something sharp. **2** a slight wound. **3** a harsh, grating sound [the *scratch* of chalk on a blackboard].

scream (skrēm) *v.* to give a loud, shrill cry, as in fright or pain [They *screamed* as the roller coaster hurtled downward.] ◆*n.* a loud, shrill cry or sound; shriek.

screen (skrēn) *n.* **1** a mesh woven loosely of wires so as to leave small openings between them. Screens are used in windows, doors, etc., to keep insects out. **2** a covered frame or curtain used to hide, separate, or protect. **3** a surface on which movies, television pictures, etc., are shown.

search·light (surch'līt) *n.* a light and reflector that can throw a strong beam of light in any direction.

seat (sēt) *n.* **1** a thing to sit on, as a chair, bench, etc. **2** a place to sit or the right to sit [to buy two *seats* for the opera; to win a *seat* in the Senate]. ◆*v.* **1** to cause to sit; put in or on a seat [*Seat* yourself quickly.] **2** to have seats for [This car *seats* six people.]

see (sē) *v.* **1** to be aware of through the eyes; have or use the sense of sight [We *saw* two birds. I don't *see* so well.] **2** to get the meaning of; understand [Do you *see* the point of the joke?] **3** to visit with [We stopped to *see* a friend.] **4** to go to for information or advice; consult [*See* a doctor about your cough.] **5** to think or try to remember [Let me *see*, where did I put that?] —**saw, seen, see'ing**

seen (sēn) *past participle of* **see**.

sen·tence (sen't'ns) *n.* a group of words used to tell, ask, command, or exclaim something, usually having a subject and a predicate. A sentence begins with a capital letter and ends with a period, question mark, or exclamation point ["I saw John." is a *sentence*. "An evening spent at home" is not a *sentence*.]

Sep·tem·ber (sep tem'bər) *n.* the ninth month of the year, which has 30 days: abbreviated **Sept.**

set (set) *v.* **1** to put in a certain place or position [*Set* the book on the table.] **2** to put in order or in the right condition, position, etc.; arrange; adjust [to *set* a trap; to *set* a thermostat; to *set* a broken bone; to *set* a table for a meal]. **3** to establish or fix, as a time for a meeting, a price, a rule, a limit, etc. **4** to sink below the horizon [The sun *sets* in the west.] —**set, set'ting** ◆*n.* **1** a number of parts put together, as in a cabinet [a TV *set*]. **2** in mathematics, any collection of units, points, numbers, etc.

set·ting (set'ing) *n.* the time, place, and circumstances of an event, story, play, etc.

searchlight

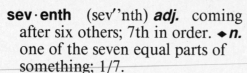

sev·enth (sev''nth) *adj.* coming after six others; 7th in order. ◆*n.* one of the seven equal parts of something; 1/7.

shad·ow (shad'ō) *n.* the darkness or the dark shape cast upon a surface by something cutting off light from it [Her large hat put her face in *shadow*. His hand cast a *shadow* on the wall.]

shadow

shape (shāp) *n.* the way a thing looks because of its outline; outer form; figure [The cloud had the *shape* of a lamb.] ◆*v.* to give a certain shape to; form [The potter *shaped* the clay into a bowl.] —**shaped, shap'ing**

share (sher) *n.* a part that each one of a group gets or has [your *share* of the cake; my *share* of the blame]. ◆*v.* to have a share of with others; have or use together [The three of you will *share* the back seat.] —**shared, shar'ing**

sharp (shärp) *adj.* **1** having a thin edge for cutting or a fine point for piercing [a *sharp* knife; a *sharp* needle]. **2** very clever or shrewd [a *sharp* mind]. ◆*adv.* exactly or promptly [She gets up at 6:30 *sharp*.] —**sharp'ly** *adv.* —**sharp'ness** *n.*

sheep (shēp) *n.* an animal that chews its cud and is related to the goat. Its body is covered with heavy wool, and its flesh is used as food, called mutton. —*pl.* **sheep**

shovel

shelf (shelf) *n.* a thin, flat length of wood, metal, etc., fastened against a wall or built into a frame so as to hold things [the top *shelf* of a bookcase]. —*pl.* **shelves**

shelves (shelvz) *n. plural of* **shelf**.

shine (shīn) *v.* **1** to give off light or reflect light; be bright [The sun *shines*. Her hair *shone*.] **2** to make bright by polishing [to *shine* shoes]. —**shone** or **shined, shin'ing** ◆*n.* the act of polishing, as shoes.

shoot (sh͞oot) *v.* to send a bullet, arrow, etc., from [to *shoot* a gun]. —**shot, shoot'ing** ◆*n.* a new growth; sprout. —**shoot'er** *n.*

short (shôrt) *adj.* **1** not measuring much from end to end or from beginning to end; not long [a *short* stick; a *short* trip; a *short* novel; a *short* wait]. **2** not tall; low [a *short* tree]. **3** less or having less than what is enough or correct [Our supply of food is *short*. We are *short* ten dollars.] **4** taking a shorter time to say than other sounds [The "e" in "bed" and the "i" in "rib" are *short*.] ◆*adv.* so as to be short [Cut your speech *short*. We fell *short* of our goal.] ◆*v.* to give less than what is needed, usual, etc. [The cashier *shorted* the customer a dollar.]

should·n't (sh͝ood''nt) should not.

shov·el (shuv''l) *n.* a tool with a broad scoop and a handle, for lifting and moving loose material. ◆*v.* to lift and move with a shovel [to *shovel* coal]. —**shov'eled** or **shov'elled, shov'el·ing** or **shov'el·ling**

show·er (shou'ər) *n.* **1** a short fall of rain or hail. ☆**2** a bath in which the body is sprayed with fine streams of water. *The full name is* **shower bath.** ◆*v.* to bathe under a shower.

shy (shī) *adj.* **1** easily frightened; timid [a *shy* animal]. **2** not at ease with other people; bashful [a *shy* child]. —**shi'er** or **shy'er, shi'est** or **shy'est** —**shy'ly** *adv.* —**shy'ness** *n.*

sigh (sī) *v.* to let out a long, deep, sounded breath, usually to show that one is sad, tired, relieved, etc. ◆*n.* the act or sound of sighing [She breathed a *sigh* of relief.]

sight (sīt) *n.* **1** something that is seen; especially, something unusual worth seeing [The Grand Canyon is a *sight* you won't forget.] **2** the ability to see; vision; eyesight [He lost his *sight* in the war.] **3** the distance over which one can see [The airplane passed out of *sight*.] ◆*v.* to see [The sailor *sighted* land.]

sign (sīn) *n.* **1** a thing or act that stands for something else; symbol [Black is worn as a *sign* of grief. She saluted the flag as a *sign* of respect. The *sign* (+) means "add."] **2** a board, card, etc., put up in a public place, with information, a warning, etc., on it [The *sign* said, "Do not enter."] **3** anything that tells of the existence or coming of something else [Red spots on the face may be a *sign* of measles.] ◆*v.* to write one's name on [to *sign* a contract to make it legal].

since (sins) *adv.* from then until now [Lynn came Monday and has been here ever *since*.] ◆*prep.* from or during the time given until now [I've been up *since* dawn.] ◆*conj.* **1** after the time that [It's been two years *since* I saw you.] **2** because [You may have these tools, *since* I no longer need them.]

sis·ter (sis′tər) *n.* a girl or woman as she is related to the other children of her parents.

sixth (siksth) *adj.* coming after five others; 6th in order. ◆*n.* one of the six equal parts of something; 1/6.

size (sīz) *n.* **1** the amount of space taken up by a thing; how large or how small a thing is [Tell me the *size* of your room. He is strong for his *size*.] **2** any of a series of measures, often numbered, for grading things [She wears a *size* 12 dress. These are jumbo *size* peanuts.] ◆*v.* to arrange according to size.
—**sized, siz′ing**

sleet (slēt) *n.* **1** rain that is partly frozen. **2** a mixture of rain and snow. ◆*v.* to shower in the form of sleet. —**sleet′y** *adj.*

slight (slīt) *adj.* small in amount or degree; not great, strong, important, etc. [a *slight* change in temperature; a *slight* advantage; a *slight* bruise]. —**slight′ly** *adv.*

slip (slip) *v.* **1** to go or pass quietly or without being noticed; escape [We *slipped* out the door. It *slipped* my mind. Time *slipped* by.] **2** to move, shift, or drop, as by accident [The plate *slipped* from my hand.] **3** to slide by accident [He *slipped* on the ice.] —**slipped, slip′ping**

slip·per (slip′ər) *n.* a light, low shoe that can be slipped on easily, especially one made to be worn indoors. —**slip′pered** *adj.*

slo·gan (slō′gən) *n.* a word or phrase used by a political party, business, etc., to get attention or to advertise a product.

slum·ber (slum′bər) *v.* **1** to sleep. **2** to be quiet or inactive [The volcano has *slumbered* for years.] ◆*n.* sleep.

sly (slī) *adj.* able to fool or trick others; cunning; crafty [the *sly* fox]. —**sli′er** or **sly′er, sli′est** or **sly′est** —**sly′ly** or **sli′ly** *adv.*

smart (smärt) *adj.* **1** intelligent or clever [a *smart* student]. **2** neat, clean, and well-groomed. **3** of the newest fashion; stylish [a *smart* new hat]. ◆*v.* to cause a sharp, stinging pain [A bee sting *smarts*.] —**smart′ly** *adv.* —**smart′ness** *n.*

smile (smīl) *v.* to show that one is pleased, happy, amused, etc., or sarcastic or scornful, by making the corners of the mouth turn up. —**smiled, smil′ing** ◆*n.* the act of smiling or the look on one's face when one smiles.

sneak·er (snē′kər) *n.* ☆a cloth shoe with a flat, rubber sole and no heel, worn for play and for sports.

slipper

a	ask, fat
ā	ape, date
ä	car, lot
e	elf, ten
er	berry, care
ē	even, meet
i	is, hit
ir	mirror, here
ī	ice, fire
ō	open, go
ô	law, horn
oi	oil, point
ōō	look, pull
ōō	ooze, tool
yōō	unite, cure
yōō	cute, few
ou	out, crowd
u	up, cut
ʉr	fur, fern
ə	a in ago
	e in agent
	e in father
	i in unity
	o in collect
	u in focus
ch	chin, arch
ng	ring, singer
sh	she, dash
th	thin, truth
th	then, father
zh	s in pleasure
′	as in (ā′b'l)

183

snow·flake (snō′flāk) *n.* a flake of snow. Snowflakes are crystals.

soak (sōk) *v.* **1** to make or become completely wet by keeping or staying in a liquid [She *soaked* her sore hand in hot water. Let the beans *soak* overnight to soften them.] **2** to suck up or absorb [Use a sponge to *soak* up that water.] ◆*n.* the act of soaking.

some (sum) *adj.* **1** being a certain one or ones not named or not known [*Some* people were playing ball.] **2** being of a certain but not a definite number or amount [Have *some* candy.] ◆*pron.* a certain number or amount, but not all [Take *some*.]

soon (sōōn) *adv.* **1** in a short time; before much time has passed [Spring will *soon* be here.] **2** fast or quickly [as *soon* as possible]. **3** ahead of time; early [She left too *soon*.]

soot (soot) *n.* a black powder formed when some things burn. It is mostly carbon and makes smoke gray or black.

soothe (sōōth) *v.* **1** to make quiet or calm by being gentle or friendly [The clerk *soothed* the angry customer with helpful answers.] **2** to take away some of the pain or sorrow of; ease [I hope this lotion will *soothe* your sunburn.] —**soothed, sooth′ing** —**sooth′ing·ly** *adv.*

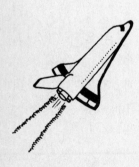

spaceship

space·ship (spās′ship) *n.* a vehicle for travel in outer space. Its movement is controlled by rockets.

speak (spēk) *v.* **1** to say something with the voice; talk [They *spoke* to each other on the phone.] **2** to make a speech [Who *speaks* first on the program?]

spe·cial (spesh′əl) *adj.* **1** not like others; different; distinctive [The cook has a *special* recipe for tacos.] **2** unusual; extraordinary [Your idea has *special* merit.] **3** more than others; chief; main [her *special* friend]. —**spe′cial·ly** *adv.*

spell (spel) *v.* to say or write in order the letters that make up a word [Can you *spell* "seize"? He *spells* badly.]

spell·ing (spel′ing) *n.* **1** the act of telling or writing the letters of a word in proper order. **2** the way in which a word is spelled.

spend (spend) *v.* to pay out or give up, as money, time, or effort [He *spent* $50 for food. Try to *spend* some time with me.] —**spent, spend′ing** —**spend′er** *n.*

spill (spil) *v.* to let flow over or run out [Who *spilled* water on the floor? Try not to *spill* any sugar.] —**spilled** or **spilt, spill′ing** ◆*n.* **1** the act of spilling. **2** a fall or tumble, as from a horse: *used only in everyday talk.*

splash (splash) *v.* **1** to make a liquid scatter and fall in drops [to *splash* water or mud about]. **2** to dash a liquid on, so as to wet or soil [The car *splashed* my coat.] —**splash′y** *adj.*

split (split) *v.* to separate or divide along the length into two or more parts [to *split* a wiener bun]. —**split, split′ting** ◆*n.* a break, crack, or tear [a *split* in the seam of a dress]. ◆*adj.* broken into parts; divided.

spray (sprā) *n.* a mist of tiny drops, as of water thrown off from a waterfall. ◆*v.* to put something on in a spray [to *spray* a car with paint]. —**spray′er** *n.*

spread (spred) *v.* **1** to open out or stretch out, in space or time [*Spread* out the tablecloth. The eagle *spread* its wings. Our trip *spread* out over two weeks.] **2** to put or cover in a thin layer [to *spread* bread with jelly]. ◆*n.* **1** a cloth cover, as for a table or bed. **2** any soft substance, as jam or butter, that can be spread in a layer. —**spread′er** *n.*

spring (spring) *v.* **1** to move suddenly and quickly; leap; jump up [I *sprang* to my feet.] **2** to snap back into position or shape, as a rubber band that is stretched and then let go. —**sprang** or **sprung, sprung, spring'ing** ◆*n.* **1** a device, as a coil of wire, that returns to its original shape when pressure on it is released. Springs are used in beds and automobiles to take up shock or in clocks, etc., to make them go. **2** water flowing up from the ground. **3** the season when plants begin to grow, between winter and summer.

staff (staf) *n.* **1** a stick, rod, or pole used for support in walking, for holding a flag, or as a weapon, a sign of authority, etc. [a bishop's *staff*]. **2** a group of people working together under a manager, chief, military officer, etc. [the teaching *staff* of a school]. **3** the five lines and the spaces between them on which music is written. —*pl.* **staffs** *The plural for meanings* 1 *and* 3 *is sometimes* **staves**.

stand (stand) *v.* **1** to be or get in an upright position on one's feet [*Stand* by your desk.] **2** to be or place in an upright position on its base, bottom, etc. [Our trophy *stands* on the shelf. *Stand* the broom in the corner.] **3** to be placed or situated [Our house *stands* on a hill.] —**stood, stand'ing**

start (stärt) *v.* **1** to begin to go, do, act, be, etc. [We *start* for Toledo today. The show *starts* at 8:30.] **2** to cause to begin; set in motion or action [*Start* the car. Who *started* the fight?] ◆*n.* the act of starting or beginning.

steel (stēl) *n.* a hard, tough metal made of iron mixed with a little carbon.

step (step) *n.* **1** the act of moving and placing the foot forward, backward, sideways, up, or down, as in walking, dancing, or climbing. **2** a place to rest the foot in going up or down, as a stair or the rung of a ladder. ◆*v.* to move by taking a step or steps. —**stepped, step'ping**

sting (sting) *v.* **1** to hurt by pricking [Wasps can *sting* you.] **2** to cause or feel sharp pain [The cold wind *stung* her cheeks.] —**stung, sting'ing** ◆*n.* the act or power of stinging [The *sting* of a bee may be dangerous.]

stone (stōn) *n.* **1** hard mineral matter that is found in the earth but is not metal; rock [a monument built of *stone*]. **2** a small piece of this [Don't throw *stones*. Rubies are precious *stones*.]

stood (stood) *past tense and past participle of* **stand**.

stop (stäp) *v.* **1** to halt or keep from going on, moving, acting, etc.; bring or come to an end [My watch *stopped*. The noise *stopped*. *Stop* the car. They *stopped* us from talking.] **2** to clog or block [The drain in the sink is *stopped* up.] **3** to stay or visit [We *stopped* there overnight.] —**stopped, stop'ping** ◆*n.* **1** a place stopped at [a *stop* on a bus route]. **2** the act or fact of stopping; finish; end [Put a *stop* to this argument.]

storm (stôrm) *n.* a strong wind along with a heavy rain, snow, etc., and, often, thunder and lightning. ◆*v.* to blow violently and rain, snow, etc.

straw·ber·ry (strô'ber'ē) *n.* the small, red, juicy fruit of a low plant of the rose family. —*pl.* **straw'ber'ries**

stream (strēm) *n.* a flow of water; especially, a small river. ◆*v.* **1** to flow in a stream. **2** to pour out or flow [eyes *streaming* with tears].

street (strēt) *n.* a road in a city or town; also, such a road with its sidewalks and buildings.

staff

a	ask, fat
ā	ape, date
ä	car, lot
e	elf, ten
er	berry, care
ē	even, meet
i	is, hit
ir	mirror, here
ī	ice, fire
ō	open, go
ô	law, horn
oi	oil, point
ʊ	look, pull
ōō	ooze, tool
yʊ	unite, cure
yōō	cute, few
ou	out, crowd
u	up, cut
ur	fur, fern
ə	a in ago
	e in agent
	e in father
	i in unity
	o in collect
	u in focus
ch	chin, arch
ng	ring, singer
sh	she, dash
th	thin, truth
th	then, father
zh	s in pleasure
'	as in (ā'b'l)

185

suit

strike (strīk) **v.** **1** to hit by giving a blow, coming against with force, etc. [Pat *struck* him in anger. The car *struck* the curb.] **2** to make a sound by hitting some part [The clock *struck* one. *Strike* middle C on the piano.] **3** to set on fire as by rubbing [to *strike* a match]. **4** to stop working until certain demands have been met [The workers are *striking* for shorter hours.] —**struck, struck** or **strick′en, strik′ing**

string (striŋ) **n.** **1** a thick thread or thin strip of cloth, leather, etc., used for tying or pulling; cord. **2** a number of things in a row [a *string* of lights]. ◆**v.** **1** to put on a string [to *string* beads]. **2** to stretch like a string; extend [to *string* telephone wires on poles; to *string* out a speech]. —**strung, string′ing**

strong (strôŋ) **adj.** **1** having great force or power; not weak; powerful [a *strong* person; *strong* winds]. **2** having a powerful effect on the senses or mind; not mild [a *strong* taste, smell, light, sound, liking, etc.] —**strong′ly** **adv.** —**strong′ness n.**

struck (struk) *past tense and a past participle of* **strike.**

stud·y (stud′ē) **v.** **1** to try to learn by reading, thinking, etc. [to *study* law]. **2** to look at or into carefully; examine or investigate [We must *study* the problem of crime.] **3** to read so as to understand and remember [to *study* a lesson]. —**stud′ied, stud′y·ing** ◆**n.** **1** a branch of learning; subject [the *study* of medicine]. **2** a room used for studying, reading, etc. —*pl.* **stud′ies**

sub·tract (səb trakt′) **v.** to take away, as a part from a whole or one number from another [If 3 is *subtracted* from 5, the remainder is 2.]

sug·ar (shoog′ər) **n.** any of certain sweet substances in the form of crystals that dissolve in water. Glucose, lactose, and sucrose are different kinds of sugar. Sucrose is the common sugar used to sweeten food.

suit (soot) **n.** a set of clothes to be worn together, especially a coat with trousers or a skirt of the same material, and sometimes a vest. ◆**v.** to meet the needs of; be right for [This color *suits* your complexion.]

sum (sum) **n.** the result got by adding together two or more numbers or quantities; total. ◆**v.** to add up and get the sum of. —**summed, sum′ming**

sure (shoor) **adj.** **1** that will not fail; safe, certain, reliable, etc. [a *sure* cure; a *sure* friend]. **2** firm or steady [Be careful to have a *sure* footing on the ladder.] **3** without doubt; certain; positive [I'm *sure* they did it.] —**sur′er, sur′est**

swarm (swôrm) **n.** **1** a large number of bees, led by a queen, leaving a hive to start a new colony. **2** a colony of bees in a hive. ◆**v.** to fly off in a swarm, as bees do.

swim (swim) **v.** to move in water by working the arms, legs, fins, etc. —**swam, swum, swim′ming** ◆**n.** an act, time, or distance of swimming. —**swim′mer n.**

take (tāk) **v.** **1** to get hold of; grasp [*Take* my hand as we cross the street.] **2** to write down; copy [*Take* notes on the lecture.] **3** to carry [*Take* your skis with you.] **4** to lead or bring [I *took* Pat to the movie. This road *takes* us to the park.] —**took, tak′en, tak′ing**

tax (taks) *n.* money that one must pay to help support a government. It is usually a percentage of one's income or of the value of something bought or owned. —**tax′a·ble** *adj.*

teach·er (tēch′ər) *n.* a person who teaches, especially in a school or college.

team (tēm) *n.* **1** two or more horses, oxen, etc., harnessed together as for pulling a plow or wagon. **2** a group of people working together or playing together in a contest against another such group [a *team* of scientists; a baseball *team*]. ◆*v.* to join together in a team [Let's *team* up with them.]

teeth (tēth) *n.* *plural of* **tooth**.

tel·e·phone (tel′ə fōn) *n.* ☆**1** a way of sending sounds over distances by changing them into electric signals which are sent through a wire and then changed back into sounds. ☆**2** a device for sending and receiving sounds in this way. ◆*v.* ☆ to talk over a telephone. —**tel′e·phoned, tel′e·phon·ing** —**tel·e·phon·ic** (tel′ə fän′ik) *adj.*

tell (tel) *v.* **1** to put into words; say [*Tell* the facts.] **2** to give the story; report; narrate [The book *tells* of their travels.] **3** to let know; inform [*Tell* me how to get there.] **4** to order or command [She *told* us to leave.]

tell·er (tel′ər) *n.* **1** a person who tells a story, etc. **2** a clerk in a bank who receives and pays out money.

tenth (tenth) *adj.* coming after nine others; 10th in order. ◆*n.* one of ten equal parts of something; 1/10.

Tex·as (tek′səs) a state in the south central part of the U.S.: abbreviated **Tex., TX** —**Tex′an** *adj., n.*

than (than *or* thən) *conj.* compared to. *Than* is used before the second part of a comparison [I am taller *than* you.]

thank (thangk) *v.* to say that one is grateful to another for a kindness [We *thanked* her for her help.]

that (that *or* thət) *pron.* **1** the person or thing mentioned [*That* is José.] **2** who, whom, or which [She's the one *that* I saw. Here's the book *that* I borrowed.] —*pl.* **those**

thaw (thô) *v.* **1** to melt [The snow *thawed*.] **2** to become unfrozen: said of frozen foods. ◆*n.* weather that is warm enough to melt snow and ice.

them (them) *pron.* the form of **they** that is used as the object of a verb or preposition [I met *them* at the airport. Give the flowers to *them*.]

there's (therz) there is.

they (thā) *pron.* **1** the persons, animals, or things being talked about [The players knew *they* had won. Put the keys back where *they* were.] **2** people in general [*They* say it can't happen.] *They* is the plural of *he, she,* or *it*.

they're (ther) they are.

think (thingk) *v.* **1** to use the mind; reason [*Think* before you act.] **2** to form or have in the mind [She was *thinking* happy thoughts.] —**thought, think′ing**

third (thurd) *adj.* coming after two others; 3rd in order. ◆*n.* one of three equal parts of something; 1/3.

thir·teen (thur′tēn′) *n., adj.* three more than ten; the number 13.

thir·ty (thur′ē) *n., adj.* three times ten; the number 30. —*pl.* **thir′ties**

thought¹ (thôt) *n.* **1** the act or process of thinking [When deep in *thought*, he doesn't hear.] **2** what one thinks; idea, opinion, plan, etc. [a penny for your *thoughts*].

Texas

a	ask, fat
ā	ape, date
ä	car, lot
e	elf, ten
er	berry, care
ē	even, meet
i	is, hit
ir	mirror, here
ī	ice, fire
ō	open, go
ô	law, horn
oi	oil, point
oo	look, pull
o͞o	ooze, tool
yoo	unite, cure
yo͞o	cute, few
ou	out, crowd
u	up, cut
ur	fur, fern
ə	a in ago
	e in agent
	e in father
	i in unity
	o in collect
	u in focus
ch	chin, arch
ng	ring, singer
sh	she, dash
th	thin, truth
th	then, father
zh	s in pleasure
′	as in (ā′b'l)

thought² (thôt) *past tense and past participle of* **think.**

thread (thred) *n.* a very thin cord used in sewing and made of strands of spun cotton, silk, etc., twisted together. ◆*v.* to put a thread through the eye of [to *thread* a needle]. —**thread'like** *adj.*

thrill (thril) *v.* to feel or make greatly excited; shiver or tingle with strong feeling [She *thrilled* at the praise. That movie *thrilled* us.] ◆*n.* a strong feeling of excitement that makes one shiver [Seeing a lion gave me a *thrill.*]

throat (thrōt) *n.* **1** the front part of the neck. **2** the upper part of the passage from the mouth to the stomach or lungs [I have a sore *throat.*]

through (thrōo) *prep.* **1** in one side and out the other side of; from end to end of [The nail went *through* the board. We drove *through* the tunnel.] **2** from the beginning to the end of [We stayed in Maine *through* the summer.] ◆*adv.* in a complete and thorough way; entirely [We were soaked *through* by the rain.] ◆*adj.* finished [Are you *through* with your homework?]

throw (thrō) *v.* to send through the air by a fast motion of the arm; hurl, toss, etc. [to *throw* a ball]. —**threw, thrown, throw'ing** ◆*n.* the act of throwing [The fast *throw* put the runner out at first base.]

thumb (thum) *n.* the short, thick finger nearest the wrist. ◆*v.* to handle, turn, soil, etc., with the thumb [to *thumb* the pages of a book].

tide (tīd) *n.* the regular rise and fall of the ocean's surface, about every twelve hours, caused by the attraction of the moon and sun. ◆*v.* to help in overcoming a time of trouble [Will ten dollars *tide* you over till Monday?] —**tid'ed, tid'ing**

toy

tie (tī) *v.* **1** to bind together or fasten with string, rope, cord, etc. [They *tied* his hands together. *Tie* the boat to the pier.] **2** to equal, as in a score [Pablo *tied* with Carmela for first place.] —**tied, ty'ing** ◆*n.* **1** *a shorter word for* **necktie. 2** the fact of being equal, as in a score; also, a contest in which scores are equal. —*pl.* **ties**

to (tōo *or* too *or* tə) *prep.* **1** in the direction of [Turn *to* the right.] **2** on, onto, against, etc. [Put your hand *to* your mouth. Apply the lotion *to* the skin.]

tone (tōn) *n.* **1** a sound, especially one that is pleasant or musical [the clear *tones* of an oboe]. **2** a way of speaking or writing that shows a certain feeling [Her answer had a friendly *tone.*] **3** a color, shade, or tint [His suit had several *tones* of brown.]

too (tōo) *adv.* **1** in addition; besides; also [You come, *too.*] **2** more than enough [This hat is *too* big.] **3** very [You are *too* kind.]

tooth (tōoth) *n.* any of the white, bony parts growing from the jaws and used for biting and chewing.

touch (tuch) *v.* **1** to put the hand, finger, etc., on something in order to feel it [He *touched* the fence to see if the paint was wet.] **2** to handle, use, or disturb [Don't *touch* the papers on my desk.] **3** to bring or come into contact with something else [She *touched* a match to the candle. The bumpers of the cars *touched.*] **4** to make feel pity, sympathy, gratitude, etc. [Your kindness *touches* me.]

town (toun) *n.* a place where there are a large number of houses and other buildings, larger than a village but smaller than a city.

toy (toi) *n.* a thing to play with; especially, a plaything for children. ◆*adj.* **1** like a toy in size or use [a *toy* dog]. **2** made for use as a toy; especially, made as a small model [a *toy* train].

track (trak) ***n.*** **1** a mark left in passing, as a footprint or wheel rut. **2** a path or trail. ◆***v.*** **1** to follow the tracks of [We *tracked* the fox to its den.] **2** to make tracks or dirty marks [The children *tracked* up the clean floor.]

tra·peze (tra pēz′) ***n.*** a short crossbar hung by two ropes, on which acrobats do stunts.

trip (trip) ***v.*** to stumble or make stumble [She *tripped* over the rug. Bill put out his foot and *tripped* me.] —**tripped, trip′ping** ◆***n.*** a traveling from one place to another and returning; journey, especially a short one.

tur·key (tur′kē) ***n.*** ☆**1** a large, wild or tame bird, originally of North America, with a small head and spreading tail. ☆**2** its flesh, used as food. —*pl.* **tur′keys** or **tur′key**

twen·ty (twen′tē) ***n., adj.*** two times ten; the number 20. —*pl.* **twen′ties**

two (to͞o) ***n., adj.*** one more than one; the number 2. —**in two,** in two parts.

Uu

un- 1 *a prefix meaning* not *or* the opposite of [An *unhappy* person is one who is not happy, but sad.] **2** *a prefix meaning* to reverse *or* undo the action of [To *untie* a shoelace is to reverse the action of tying it.]

un·a·ble (un ā′b'l) ***adj.*** not able; not having the means or power to do something.

un·but·ton (un but′'n) ***v.*** to unfasten the button or buttons of.

un·clean (un klēn′) ***adj.*** dirty; filthy.

un·der (un′dər) ***prep.*** in or to a place, position, amount, value, etc., lower than; below [He sang *under* her window. It rolled *under* the table. It weighs *under* a pound.] ◆***adv.*** less in amount, value, etc. [It cost two dollars or *under*.]

un·e·ven (un ē′vən) ***adj.*** not even, level, or smooth; irregular [*uneven* ground]. —**un·e′ven·ly *adv.*** —**un·e′ven·ness *n.***

un·load (un lōd′) ***v.*** to take a load or cargo from a truck, ship, etc.

un·luck·y (un luk′ē) ***adj.*** having or bringing bad luck; not lucky; unfortunate [There is a superstition that breaking a mirror is *unlucky*.] —**un·luck′i·er, un·luck′i·est** —**un·luck′i·ly *adv.***

un·paid (un pād′) ***adj.*** not receiving pay [an *unpaid* helper].

un·true (un tro͞o′) ***adj.*** **1** not correct; false. **2** not faithful or loyal. —**un·tru′ly *adv.***

un·wrap (un rap′) ***v.*** to open by taking off the wrapping; also, to become opened in this way. —**un·wrapped′, un·wrap′ping**

use (yo͞oz) ***v.*** **1** to put or bring into service or action [*Use* the vacuum cleaner on the rugs. What kind of toothpaste do you *use*?] **2** to do away with by using; consume [She *used* up all the soap. Don't *use* up your energy.] —**used, us′ing**

used (yo͞ozd) ***adj.*** that has been used; not new; secondhand [*used* cars].

Vv

verb (vurb) ***n.*** a word that shows action or a condition of being [In the sentence "The children ate early and were asleep by seven o'clock," the words "ate" and "were" are *verbs*.]

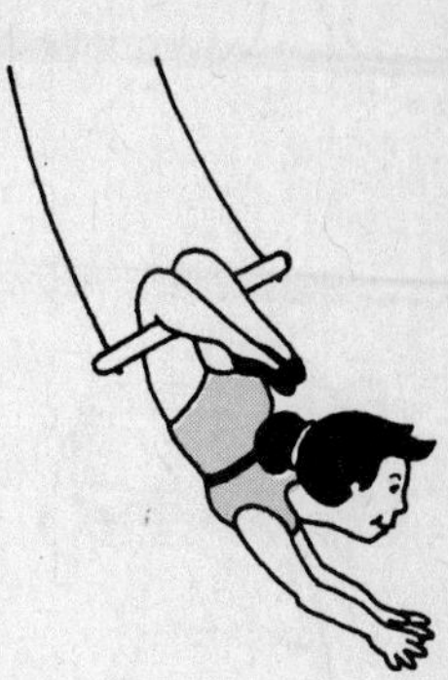

trapeze

a	ask, fat
ā	ape, date
ä	car, lot
e	elf, ten
er	berry, care
ē	even, meet
i	is, hit
ir	mirror, here
ī	ice, fire
ō	open, go
ô	law, horn
oi	oil, point
oo	look, pull
o͞o	ooze, tool
yoo	unite, cure
yo͞o	cute, few
ou	out, crowd
u	up, cut
ur	fur, fern
ə	a in ago
	e in agent
	e in father
	i in unity
	o in collect
	u in focus
ch	chin, arch
ŋ	ring, singer
sh	she, dash
th	thin, truth
th	then, father
zh	s in pleasure
′	as in (ā′b'l)

ver·y (ver′ē) *adv.* in a high degree; to a great extent; extremely [*very* cold; *very* funny; *very* sad].

vest (vest) *n.* a short garment without sleeves, worn usually under a suit coat.

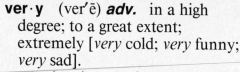

wagon

wag·on (wag′ən) *n.* a vehicle with four wheels, especially for carrying heavy loads.

wal·let (wäl′it *or* wôl′it) *n.* ☆a thin, flat case for carrying money, cards, etc., in the pocket.

was (wuz *or* wäz) *the form of* be *showing the past time with singular nouns and with* I, he, she, *or* it.

was·n't (wuz′′nt *or* wäz′′nt) was not.

watch (wäch *or* wôch) *v.* 1 to keep one's sight on; look at [We *watched* the parade.] 2 to take care of; look after; guard [The shepherd *watched* his flock.] ◆*n.* 1 the act of watching or guarding [The dog keeps *watch* over the house.] 2 a device for telling time that is like a clock but small enough to be worn, as on the wrist, or carried in the pocket.

wa·ter (wôt′ər) *n.* the colorless liquid that falls as rain, is found in springs, rivers, lakes, and oceans, and forms a large part of the cells of all living things. It is made up of hydrogen and oxygen, with the chemical formula H_2O. ◆*v.* 1 to give water to [to *water* a horse]. 2 to supply with water, as by sprinkling [to *water* a lawn].

☆water bed a bed that is a plastic bag filled with water and held in a frame.

wa·ter·mel·on (wôt′ər mel′ən) *n.* a large melon with a green rind and juicy, red pulp with many seeds.

whale

wa·ter·proof (wôt′ər prōōf) *adj.* treated with rubber, plastic, etc., so that water cannot come through [a *waterproof* raincoat]. ◆*v.* to make waterproof.

wax (waks) *n.* 1 a yellow substance that bees make and use for building honeycombs; beeswax. 2 any substance like this, as paraffin. Wax is used to make candles, polishes, etc. ◆*v.* to put wax or polish on.

wear (wer) *v.* 1 to have or carry on the body [*Wear* your coat. Do you *wear* glasses?] 2 to have or show in the way one appears [She *wore* a frown. He *wears* his hair long.] 3 to make or become damaged, used up, etc. by use or friction [She *wore* her jeans to rags. The water is *wearing* away the river bank.] —wore, worn, wear′ing

weight (wāt) *n.* 1 heaviness, the quality a thing has because of the pull of gravity on it. 2 amount of heaviness [What is your *weight*?] 3 any solid mass used for its heaviness [to lift *weights* for exercise; a paper*weight*.]

we'll (wēl) 1 we shall. 2 we will.

wet (wet) *adj.* covered or soaked with water or some other liquid [Wipe it off with a *wet* rag.] —wet′ter, wet′test

whack (hwak) *v.* to hit or slap with a sharp sound. ◆*n.* a blow that makes a sharp sound; also, this sound.

whale (hwāl) *n.* a very large mammal that lives in the sea and looks like a fish. Whales are valued for their oil. *See the picture.* ◆*v.* to hunt for whales. —whaled, whal′ing

wheel (hwēl) *n.* a round disk or frame that turns on an axle fixed at its center [a wagon *wheel*]. ◆*v.* to move on wheels or in a vehicle with wheels [to *wheel* a grocery cart].

wheth·er (hwe*th*′ər) *conj.* **1** if it is true or likely that [I don't know *whether* I can go.] **2** in either case that [It makes no difference *whether* he comes or not.]

which (hwich) *pron.* what one or what ones of those being talked about or suggested [*Which* will you choose?]

while (hwīl) *n.* a period of time [I waited a short *while*.] ◆*conj.* during the time that [I read a book *while* I waited.]

whisk (hwisk) *v.* to move, brush, etc., with a quick, sweeping motion [He *whisked* the lint from his coat with a brush.] ◆*n.* **1** a small broom with a short handle, for brushing clothes: *the full name is* **whisk broom**. **2** a kitchen tool made up of wire loops fixed in a handle, for whipping eggs, etc.

whisper (hwis′pər) *v.* to speak or say in a low, soft voice, especially without vibrating the vocal cords. ◆*n.* soft, low tone of voice [to speak in a *whisper*].

who (hoo) *pron.* what person or persons? [*Who* helped you?]

whole (hōl) *adj.* **1** not divided or cut up; in one piece [Put *whole* carrots in the stew.] **2** having all its parts, complete [The *whole* opera is on two records.] ◆*n.* the total amount [He saved the *whole* of his allowance.] —**whole′ness** *n.*

wife (wīf) *n.* the woman to whom a man is married; married woman. —*pl.* **wives**

will (wil) a helping verb used with other verbs in speaking of the future [She *will* be here soon. *Will* you ever learn?]

win·ner (win′ər) *n.* **1** one that wins. **2** a person who seems very likely to win or be successful: *used only in everyday talk.*

wire (wīr) *n.* metal that has been pulled into a very long, thin thread; also, a piece of this [*Wire* is used for carrying electric current, for making fences, for tying bales, etc.] ◆*v.* to fasten with wire [to *wire* a vine to a stake]. —**wired, wir′ing**

wives (wīvz) *n. plural of* **wife**.

wolf (woolf) *n.* **1** a wild animal that looks like a dog. It kills other animals for food. **2** a person who is fierce, cruel, greedy, etc. —*pl.* **wolves**

wolves (woolvz) *n. plural of* **wolf**.

wom·an (woom′ən) *n.* **1** an adult, female human being. **2** women as a group —*pl.* **wom′en**

wom·en (wim′in) *n. plural of* **woman**.

won't (wōnt) will not.

wood·en (wood′'n) *adj.* made of wood.

wool (wool) *n.* **1** the soft, curly hair of sheep or the hair of some other animals, as the goat or llama. **2** yarn, cloth, or clothing made from such hair.

wore (wôr) *past tense of* **wear**.

work (wurk) *n.* **1** the use of energy or skill in doing or making something; labor [Chopping wood is hard *work*.] **2** what one does to earn a living; occupation, trade, profession, etc. [His *work* is teaching.] **3** something to be done; task [She had to bring some *work* home from the office.] ◆*v.* **1** to use effort or energy to do or make something; labor; toil. **2** to have a job for pay; be employed [She *works* in a laboratory.] **3** to make or shape [*Work* the clay into a ball.] **4** to solve, as a problem. —**worked, work′ing**

work·book (wurk′book) *n.* ☆a book that has questions and exercises to be worked out by students.

wolf

a	ask, fat
ā	ape, date
ä	car, lot
e	elf, ten
er	berry, care
ē	even, meet
i	is, hit
ir	mirror, here
ī	ice, fire
ō	open, go
ô	law, horn
oi	oil, point
oo	look, pull
ōō	ooze, tool
yoo	unite, cure
yōō	cute, few
ou	out, crowd
u	up, cut
ur	fur, fern
ə	a in ago
	e in agent
	e in father
	i in unity
	o in collect
	u in focus
ch	chin, arch
ng	ring, singer
sh	she, dash
th	thin, truth
th	then, father
zh	s in pleasure
′	as in (ā′b'l)

wor·ry (wur′ē) **v.** to be or make troubled in mind; feel or make uneasy or anxious [Don't *worry.* Her absence *worried* us.] —**wor′ried, wor′ry·ing** ◆**n.** a troubled feeling; anxiety; care [sick with *worry*]. —*pl.* **wor′ries**

would (wood) *the past tense of* **will** [He promised that he *would* return.]

would·n't (wood′'nt) would not.

wrap (rap) **v. 1** to wind or fold around something [She *wrapped* a scarf around her head.] **2** to cover in this way [They *wrapped* the baby in a blanket.] **3** to cover with paper, etc. [to *wrap* a present]. —**wrapped** or **wrapt** (rapt), **wrap′ping** ◆**n.** an outer covering or outer garment [Put your *wraps* in the closet.]

wreck (rek) **n.** the remains of something that has been destroyed or badly damaged [an old *wreck* stranded on the reef]. ◆**v.** to destroy or damage badly; ruin [to *wreck* a car in an accident; to *wreck* one's plans for a picnic].

wren (ren) **n.** a small songbird with a long bill and a stubby tail that tilts up.

write (rīt) **v. 1** to form words, letters, etc., as with a pen or pencil. **2** to form the words, letters, etc., of [*Write* your address here.] **3** to be the author or composer of [Dickens *wrote* novels. Mozart *wrote* symphonies.] **4** to fill in or cover with writing [to *write* a check; to *write* ten pages]. **5** to send a message in writing; write a letter [*Write* me every week. He *wrote* that he was ill.] —**wrote, writ′ten, writ′ing**

writ·er (rīt′ər) **n.** a person who writes, especially one whose work is writing books, essays, articles, etc.; author.

wrong (rông) **adj. 1** not right, just, or good; unlawful, wicked, or bad [It is *wrong* to steal.] **2** not the one that is true, correct, wanted, etc. [the *wrong* answer].

3 in error; mistaken [He's not *wrong.*] ◆**n.** something wrong; especially, a wicked or unjust act [Does she know right from *wrong*?] ◆**adv.** in a wrong way, direction, etc.; incorrectly [You did it *wrong.*] —**wrong′ly adv.** —**wrong′ness n.**

wrote (rōt) *past tense of* **write.**

Yy

year (yir) **n. 1** a period of 365 days, or, in leap year, 366, divided into 12 months and beginning January 1. It is based on the time taken by the earth to go completely around the sun, about 365 1/4 days. **2** any period of twelve months starting at any time [She was six *years* old in July.]

yell (yel) **v.** to cry out loudly; scream. ◆**n. 1** a loud shout. **2** a cheer by a crowd, usually in rhythm, as at a football game.

your (yoor) ***pron.*** of you or done by you. *This possessive form of* **you** *is used before a noun and thought of as an adjective* [*your* book; *your* work]. *See also* **yours.**

you're (yoor *or* yōōr) you are.

yours (yoorz) ***pron.*** the one or the ones that belong to you. *This form of* **your** *is used when it is not followed by a noun* [Is this pen *yours? Yours* cost more than ours.] *Yours is used as a polite closing of a letter, often with truly, sincerely, etc.*

your·self (yər self′) ***pron.*** **1** your own self. *This form of* **you** *is used when the object is the same as the subject of the verb* [Did you cut *yourself*?] **2** your usual or true self [You are not *yourself* today.] *Yourself is also used to give force to the subject* [You *yourself* told me so.] —*pl.* **your·selves** (yər selvz′)

you've (yōōv) you have.

wren